CHAPTER 6: HARVESTING THE EARTH

6.1 *Is rock useful?*	96	
6.2 *Metals from rocks*	98	
6.3 *An ancient and cheap metal*	100	
6.4 *A modern, clean and expensive metal*	102	
6.5 *Getting to know copper*	104	
6.6 *Concrete and glass from rocks*	106	
6.7 *Black gold?*	108	

6.8 *Helpful hydrocarbons*	110
6.9 *Comparing hydrocarbons*	112
6.10 *Better safe than sorry*	114
6.11 *What's in the cracker?*	116
6.12 *Wonderful plastics*	118
6.13 *Making a car*	120

CHAPTER 7: THE EARTH AS A ROLLER-COASTER

7.1 *Non-stop Earth*	122
7.2 *Stick them together again*	124
7.3 *Cool it and make it*	126
7.4 *All change*	128

7.5 *Need a new map?*	130
7.6 *Sitting in the middle of a plate*	132
Section B: Questions	134

SECTION C: PATTERNS OF BEHAVIOUR

CHAPTER 8: CONTROLLING CHEMICAL REACTIONS

8.1 *Quick and slow*	140
8.2 *Control your speed*	142
8.3 *It's all about collisions*	144
8.4 *Investigating rates of reaction*	146
8.5 *Catalysts*	148

8.6 *Bakers and brewers*	150
8.7 *Things are hotting up*	152
8.8 *Current chemistry*	154
8.9 *Splitting salt and coating copper*	156

CHAPTER 9: MAKING MORE USE OF REACTIONS

9.1 *Mind your language*	158
9.2 *Too small to count*	160
9.3 *How much is useful?*	162

9.4 *The Reedroc ten*	164
Section C: Questions	166

Data section	168
Glossary	176

Heinemann Educational Publishers
Halley Court, Jordan Hill, Oxford, OX2 8EJ
a division of Reed Educational & Professional Publishing Ltd

OXFORD PORTSMOUTH NH (USA) CHICAGO
MELBOURNE AUCKLAND IBADAN
GABORONE JOHANNESBURG BLANTYRE

© Andrew Bethell, John Dexter, Mike Griffiths, 1996

First published 1996

ISBN 0 435 58003 5

00
10 9 8 7 6 5

Designed and typeset by Ken Vail Graphic Design

Edited by Sarah Ware

Illustrated by: Simon Girling & Associates (Mike Lacey),
        Nick Hawken, John Plumb,
        Ken Vail Graphic Design (Matt Clubb,
        Graeme Morris, Andrew Sharpe)

Cover design by Ken Vail Graphic Design

Cover photo by SPL/J. Schad (Inset: SPL/R. Ressmeyer)

Printed in Great Britain by
Bath Press Colourbooks, Glasgow

Acknowledgements

The authors and publishers would like to thank the
following for permission to use photographs:

p 2 T: John Walmsley. **p 2 B:** Anthony Blake. **p 3 T:** SPL/Larry Mulvehill.
p 3 B: Robert Harding. **p 6:** Trevor Clifford. **p 7 T:** Chris Honeywell.
p 7 B: J. Allan Cash Ltd. **p 8 T:** SPL/Peter Thorne, Johnson Matthey.
p 8 B: Holt Studios/Nigel Cattlin. **p 9:** J. Allan Cash Ltd. **p 10:** Quadrant.
p 11 T: SPL/P. Plailly. **p 11 M:** Image Select/Ann Ronan. **p 11 B:** J. Allan Cash
Ltd. **p 14 T:** FLPA/C. Carvalho. **p 14 B:** FLPA/Panola/G. Tomarchio.
p 17: Tony Gudgeon. **p 18:** J. Allan Cash Ltd. **p 19:** Allsport/Andrew
Redington. **p 20 T:** Image Select/Ann Ronan. **p 20 B:** The Defence Picture
Library. **p 22:** FLPA/Maurice Nimmo. **p 23:** Trevor Clifford.
p 24 T: SPL/ESA/DLI. **p24 BL:** J. Allan Cash Ltd. **p 24 BR:** Image Select/Ann
Ronan. **p 26 T:** Image Select/Ann Ronan. **p 26 B:** Robert Harding.
p 28 T: SPL/Prof. Erwin Mueller. **p 28 B:** Aerofilms. **p 34 T:** Allsport/Mike
Powell. **p 34 B:** Image Select/Ann Ronan. **p 36:** J. Allan Cash Ltd.
p 38 T: Peter Gould. **p 38 B:** Robert Harding. **p 40:** Peter Gould. **p 41:** Chris
Honeywell. **p 42 T:** J. Allan Cash Ltd. **p 42 B:** Trevor Clifford. **p 44 T:** Imperial
War Museum. **p 44 B:** Trevor Clifford. **p 45:** Peter Gould. **p 46 T:** Trevor
Clifford. **p 46 B:** John Walmsley. **p 47 L:** FLPA/H. Clarke.
p 47 R: SPL/Biophoto Associates. **p 48–9:** J. Allan Cash Ltd. **p 50:** Action-
Plus/Mike Hewitt. **p 54:** Zefa Picture Library. **p 55:** Peter Gould.
p 56: SPL/Jerome Yeats. **p 57:** SPL/Hank Morgan. **p 58:** Frank Lane Picture
Agency/W T Davidson. **p 59:** Seaco Picture Library. **p 61:** Peter Gould.
p 62 R: Peter Gould. **p 62 L:** Chris Honeywell. **p 63:** Peter Gould. **p 65 T:** The
Environmental Picture Library/Jerome Whittingham. **p 65 B:** Peter Gould.
p 67: Ecoscene. **p 69:** Peter Gould. **p 70:** J. Allan Cash Ltd. **p 71:** Chris
Honeywell. **p 73 R:** J. Allan Cash Ltd. **p73 L & B:** Ancient Art & Architecture
Collection. **p 74 T:** Peter Gould. **p 74 B:** FLPA. **p 76:** NHPA/David Woodfall.
p 78 L: SPL/Mark Clarke. **p 78 R:** Allsport/Clive Brunskill. **p 80 T:** SPL/David
Taylor. **p 80 B:** SPL/Roger Ressmeyer, Starlight. **p 81 T:** J. Allan Cash Ltd.
p 81 B: SPL/Amy Trustram Eve. **p 83:** Holt Studios International.
p 83 R: Peugeot. **p 83 L:** SPL/Hank Morgan. **p 83 M:** SPL/Tim Davis.
p 84: Peter Gould. **p 85:** SPL/Richard Folwell. **p 86 T & M:** Thames Water.
p 86 B: J. Allan Cash Ltd. **p 88:** Holt Studios International.
p 89 T: FLPA/Maurice Walker. **p 89 B:** Holt Studios International.
p 90 T: GeoScience Features. **p 90 B & p 91:** Holt Studios International.
p 92 TR: Sally & Richard Greenhill. **p 92 BR:** Holt Studios International.
p 92 L: BASF. **p 94 T:** J. Allan Cash Ltd. **p 94 M & B:** Holt Studios
International. **p 95:** Ecoscene/Joel Creed. **p 96:** Woodmansterne. **p 97 T:** Zefa
Picture Library. **p 97 BL & R:** GeoScience Features. **p 98:** J. Allan Cash Ltd.
p 99: U.S. Navy. **p 100:** J. Allan Cash Ltd. **p 101 T:** Zefa Picture Library.
p 101 B: John Walmsley. **p 102–3:** J. Allan Cash Ltd. **p 104 T:** Bridgeman Art
Library/Christie's. **p 104 M:** Trevor Hill. **p 104 B:** Peter Gould.
p 106 T: J. Allan Cash Ltd. **p 106 B:** Q A Photos Ltd. **p 107:** J. Allan Cash Ltd.
p 110 L: Camping Gaz. **p 110 R:** Peter Gould. **p113:** Allsport/Ben Radford.
p115: Peter Gould. **p 117 R:** Trevor Clifford. **p 117 L:** Stephen Lock.
p 118: Trevor Clifford. **p 119 T:** Allsport/Pascal Rondeau. **p 119 M:** J. Allan
Cash Ltd. **p 119 B:** Chris Honeywell. **p 122 T:** Gamma Press/Frank Spooner
Pictures. **p 122 B:** British Geological Survey. **p 123:** NHPA/David Woodfall.
p 124–6: GeoScience Features. **p 128:** J. Allan Cash Ltd. **p 130:** GeoScience
Features. **p 131:** Still Pictures/Mark Edwards. **p 132:** Planet Earth Pictures.
p 140 R: Allsport. **p 140 L:** Quadrant Picture Library. **p 140 B:** Peter Gould.
p 141 T: SPL/NASA. **p 141 B:** FLPA. **p 143:** Frank Spooner.
p 146: Allsport/John Gichigi. **p 148:** Trevor Clifford. **p 149 T:** Anthony Blake
Photo Library. **p 149 B & p 150:** Chris Honeywell. **p 151 T:** Anthony Blake
Photo Library. **p 151 B & p 153:** Chris Honeywell. **p155:** Allsport.
p 156: J. Allan Cash Ltd. **p 157:** Wm. Canning Ltd. **p 158 T:** Sally & Richard
Greenhill. **p 158 B:** J. Allan Cash Ltd. **p 159:** Trevor Clifford.
p 162 T: GeoScience Features. **p 162 B:** J. Allan Cash Ltd. **p 164:** Trevor
Clifford. **p 165:** Still Pictures/Mark Edwards.

The authors and publishers would like to thank the
following for permission to use copyright material:

p109 T: newspaper extract from *The Daily Telegraph*, London, 1996.
p 109 B: MATT cartoon from *The Daily Telegraph*, London, 1991.
p 163: information on fertiliser from Homebase.

The publishers have made every effort to trace the
copyright holders, but if they have inadvertently
overlooked any, they will be pleased to make the necessary
arrangements at the first opportunity.

How to use this book

Heinemann Coordinated Science: Chemistry has been written for your GCSE course and contains all the information you will need over the next two years for your exam syllabus.

This book has three sections. Each section matches one of the major themes in the National Curriculum.

What is in a section?

The sections are organised into double-page spreads. Each spread has:

Colour coded sections so you can quickly find the one you want.

Clear text and pictures to explain the science.

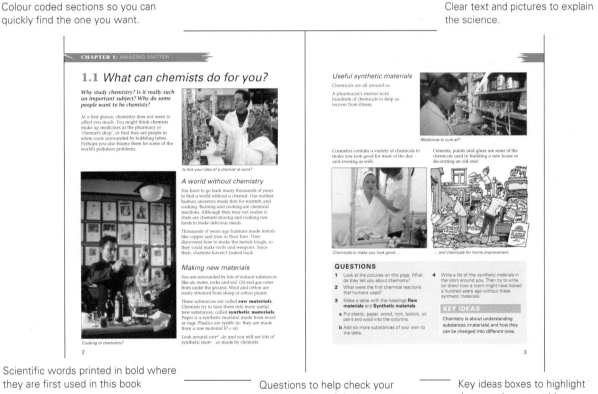

Scientific words printed in bold where they are first used in this book

Questions to help check your understanding of the important ideas on the spread.

Key ideas boxes to highlight the most important ideas on the spread

Section questions

At the end of each section, there are double-page spreads of longer questions. These are to help you find out if you understand the key ideas in that section. They can also help you revise.

Data section

There are also four double-page spreads to help you with data handling skills, like plotting graphs.

Glossary

At the back of the book is a glossary. This contains an explanation for each of the scientific words printed in bold in the book. The words are arranged alphabetically.

Assessment and resource pack

All the answers for questions in this book are in the *Heinemann Coordinated Science: Foundation Chemistry Assessment and resource pack.*

1.1 *What can chemists do for you?*

Why study chemistry? Is it really such an important subject? Why do some people want to be chemists?

At a first glance, chemistry does not seem to affect you much. You might think chemists make up medicines at the pharmacy or 'chemist's shop', or that they are people in white coats surrounded by bubbling tubes. Perhaps you also blame them for some of the world's pollution problems.

Is this your idea of a chemist at work?

A world without chemistry

You have to go back many thousands of years to find a world without a chemist. Our earliest human ancestors made fires for warmth and cooking. Burning and cooking are chemical reactions. Although they may not realise it, chefs are chemists mixing and cooking raw foods to make delicious meals.

Thousands of years ago humans made metals like copper and iron in their fires. They discovered how to make the metals tough, so they could make tools and weapons. Since then, chemists haven't looked back.

Making new materials

You are surrounded by lots of natural substances like air, water, rocks and soil. Oil and gas come from under the ground. Wool and cotton are easily obtained from sheep or cotton plants.

These substances are called **raw materials**. Chemists try to turn them into more useful new substances, called **synthetic materials**. Paper is a synthetic material made from wood or rags. Plastics are synthetic: they are made from a raw material like oil.

Look around carefully and you will see lots of synthetic materials made by chemists.

Cooking or chemistry?

Useful synthetic materials

Chemicals are all around us.

A pharmacist's shelves hold hundreds of chemicals to help us recover from illness.

Medicines to cure all?

Cosmetics contain a variety of chemicals to make you look good for most of the day – and evening as well.

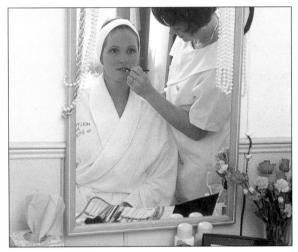

Chemicals to make you look good ...

Cements, paints and glues are some of the chemicals used in building a new house or decorating an old one!

... and chemicals for home improvement.

QUESTIONS

1 Look at the pictures on this page. What do they tell you about chemistry?

2 What were the first chemical reactions that humans used?

3 Make a table with the headings **Raw materials** and **Synthetic materials**.

 a Put plastic, paper, wood, rock, lipstick, oil, paint and wool into the columns.

 b Add six more substances of your own to the table.

4 Write a list of the *synthetic* materials in the room around you. Then try to write (or draw) how a room might have looked a hundred years ago without these synthetic materials.

KEY IDEAS

Chemistry is about understanding substances (materials) and how they can be changed into different ones.

1.2 Millions of materials

Over four million chemicals have been made or found in the world so far. If this book contained a page about each one, the book would be 240 metres thick!

All chemicals are different. They are used to make different materials. Some may cure illness – for example, paracetamol helps a headache go away. Some, like diamond, look beautiful. Others don't look attractive. Steel and concrete are tough and can be used for building. Glass is also used in buildings, but it is brittle and cracks easily.

Words like 'tough' or 'brittle' describe what a material is like. They are called its **properties**. For example, glass is transparent and brittle. Steel is hard, strong and it lets electricity travel through it.

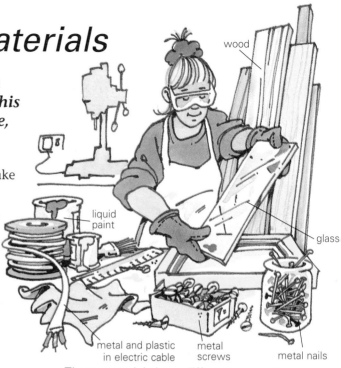

wood

liquid paint

glass

metal and plastic in electric cable

metal screws

metal nails

These materials have different properties for different purposes.

Distilled Water

RED WINE

WASHING POWDER

Granulated SUGAR

GOLDEN SYRUP

BREAKFAST CEREALS

with ADDED VITAMINS

SODA CRYSTALS

GLUCOSE POWDER

Fruit Yoghurt

Mixtures or pure substances?

Pure things and mixtures

If you swim in the sea, you can taste the salt in the water. In a swimming pool, you may taste or smell the chlorine in the water. Tap water is different from pool or sea water. Distilled water for car batteries or steam irons is different again – nothing else is in the water.

Sea, pool, tap and distilled water all contain water, but only distilled water is pure. A **pure substance** is a single substance with nothing else mixed in. Sea, pool and tap water are all **mixtures** of water and other things.

Air is a mixture of gases like oxygen, nitrogen and carbon dioxide. Soil, wood, rocks and all living things contain mixtures. Mixtures usually have the properties of the things inside them. You can see the water and also taste the salt in sea water.

Sometimes you can see the different parts of a mixture. For instance, you can pick out the different bits of fruit and cereal in muesli.

Handling chemicals safely

Some properties of substances make them dangerous.
There are special symbols to warn you about the dangers
of any substances you handle at home or at school.

Dishwasher powder and
sulphuric acid burn into
clothes and skin. They
are *corrosive*.

Petrol, alcohol and
some paints burn.
They are *flammable*.

Some weedkillers can help
things burn easily. They
are *oxidising* substances.

Pesticides and arsenic
may cause death if they
get in your body. They are
poisonous or *toxic*.

Lots of stain removers are
harmful even if not toxic.

Some materials are
irritants and may cause
a rash on your skin.

QUESTIONS

1 What are the properties of:

  a steel   **b** glass?

2 How would you describe what the
following things are like:

  a air   **b** water

  c tea   **d** sugar

  e brick   **f** a bath sponge?

3 Look at page 4 and make a list of:

  a four pure substances

  b four mixtures.

4 What are the hazards of:

  a sulphuric acid   **b** arsenic

  c petrol   **d** weedkiller?

KEY IDEAS

Mixtures contain different chemicals.

Pure substances contain a single
substance only.

Hazard symbols warn you about
the dangers of some substances.

1.3 *Stir it up and what do you get?*

What do you get when you put salt in the vegetable water? Mixing salt, coffee or ink with a liquid makes a special kind of mixture.

A good cup of coffee

Coffee beans are solid and not very pleasant to eat. Mixing them with water in the right way makes an enjoyable cup of coffee.

Salt in the vegetables

If you put a pinch of salt in the water before you cook potatoes, the salt disappears in the water. You can taste the salt in the water and later in the potatoes. The salt has mixed with the water.

Salt and water make a mixture called a **solution**. The salt has **dissolved** in the water. The salt solution looks just like water, but the water is no longer pure. The substance that does the dissolving (the water in this case) is called the **solvent**. The substance that dissolves is called the **solute**. Salt is described as being **soluble** in water – it can dissolve. There has to be enough solvent for all of the solute to dissolve.

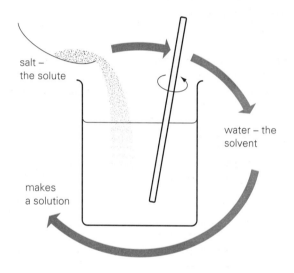

salt –
the solute

water – the
solvent

makes
a solution

Mixing a solution.

Useful solutions

Soaps and detergents dissolve in water to make a solution that cleans. The stains on your hands or clothes dissolve easily in the soapy water. The soap is easier to dissolve if it is in small flakes. The dirt dissolves more easily if the water is hot and you keep scrubbing the clothes.

It is easier to make any solution if the solute is in *small pieces*, if the solvent is *hot* and if the mixture is *stirred*. The diagram shows how you can test this idea.

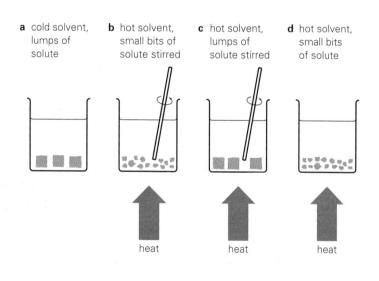

a cold solvent, lumps of solute

b hot solvent, small bits of solute stirred

c hot solvent, lumps of solute stirred

d hot solvent, small bits of solute

heat

heat

heat

Which is the easiest to mix?

Other solvents

Water isn't the only solvent you can get.

Some stains, like oil and biro ink, dissolve much better in other liquids known as dry-cleaning fluids. Gloss paint stains on brushes will dissolve in white spirit. Nail polish is removed with the chemical solvent propanone.

Solutions for life

Lemonade is a solution of sugar, lemon flavour and carbon dioxide gas in water. Tea, coffee, wine and beer are also solutions. Your blood is a complicated mixture which includes the chemical glucose (sugar) in water. Fish can only survive in water because oxygen gas dissolves in water. Fish take in this oxygen through their gills.

Drinks are solutions.

Not everything dissolves

Some things don't dissolve in a particular solvent.

Sand is **insoluble** in water and so are chalk, iron and diamond. Biro ink is insoluble in water, but it will dissolve in dry cleaning fluid. If you shake chalky water, it goes cloudy – this is called a **suspension**. A suspension is a mixture of a liquid and tiny bits of an *insoluble* solid.

The beach does not dissolve in the sea.

QUESTIONS

1 Make a list of the solutions found on these two pages.

2 You find that a biro stain doesn't wash out of your shirt. What are you going to do to remove it? Why?

3 How can we tell that river water contains dissolved oxygen?

1.4 *Making things pure*

During the gold rush in the western USA, prospectors went panning for gold. Some were lucky – they found pure gold and became rich. Making pure things from mixtures is not so easy.

Pure gold!

In some places you can mine pure gemstones like diamonds, but you can't just dig up pieces of iron or aluminium to make cars or planes. Most useful substances have to be taken out of the ground or removed from plants – they are **extracted**. They are then separated from the bits you don't want – they are **purified**.

Anyone for coffee?

Coffee beans are not very tasty. They contain coffee and lots of other substances. The coffee flavour has to be taken out of them. The beans are crushed or ground. The flavour then gets out if you mix the bits with hot water. The bits you don't want get separated out by **filtering**. Filtering separates the flavour that dissolves from the bits that don't dissolve.

You have to crush, mix and filter to get a good cup of coffee.

Filtering is used in the water industry to help make clean water. It is used in brewing to separate the beer from the mash. In the laboratory, you might separate soil and sand from rock salt by filtering.

soil and sand get trapped here

funnel

filter paper

mixture to be separated – rock salt, water, soil and sand

water with dissolved salt

Filtering separates a liquid from a solid.

Salt from the sea

You won't separate salt from water by filtering. The dissolved salt goes through the paper.

You can get the salt by **evaporating** the water with a Bunsen burner. The best salt crystals are made by boiling most of the water away and then leaving it to evaporate slowly. This is called **crystallisation**.

Heat from the sun evaporates sea water and leaves salt behind.

What about mixtures of liquids?

Wine, whisky and brandy are all mixtures of water and alcohol, with various additional flavours. The alcohol and water mix completely, so you can't see the separate liquids. Crude oil from an oil well is a mixture of hundreds of different materials.

Petrol can be obtained from oil, or alcohol from a mixture of alcohol and water, by **distillation**. This is a way of separating a mixture of liquids by boiling and then cooling them down.

Drinks like whisky are made by distillation. Distillation makes the alcohol stronger.

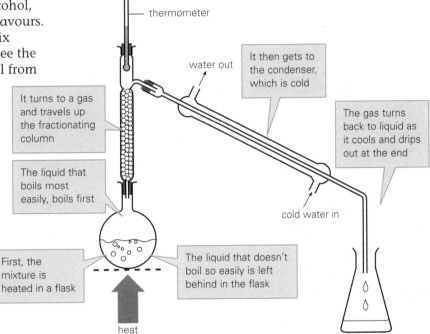

thermometer

water out

It then gets to the condenser, which is cold

It turns to a gas and travels up the fractionating column

The gas turns back to liquid as it cools and drips out at the end

The liquid that boils most easily, boils first

cold water in

First, the mixture is heated in a flask

The liquid that doesn't boil so easily is left behind in the flask

heat

Distillation is used to separate liquids with different boiling points.

QUESTIONS

1 How would you separate:
   a salt from a glass of salty water
   b bits of chalk from some pond water?

2 **a** How is salt obtained in some hot countries?
   b Why isn't it done like this in Britain?

3 Why is whisky made by distillation?

1.5 *Separating and analysing*

If you are ill, a blood test can tell doctors what germs are inside you. A car's exhaust gets tested to make sure it's not polluting the air. How do you find out what's in things?

Finding out what something is made of is called **analysis**. In factories, all sorts of products (like pet foods, fertilisers, steel or medicines) are analysed to make sure they contain only the right ingredients.

Chromatography

If you are careless enough to let the rain get to your homework, the ink might run. Sometimes new colours appear as the ink runs, especially if you've used some felt-tip pens. It happens because ink is made from different coloured dyes.

A process like this called **chromatography** can be used to find out the different dyes in any coloured material.

A car's exhaust fumes get analysed.

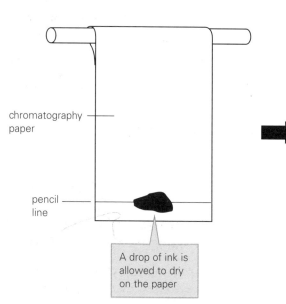
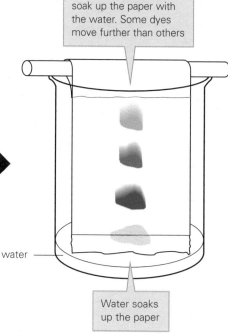

The separate colours of the ink spot gradually soak up the paper with the water. Some dyes move further than others

chromatography paper

pencil line

A drop of ink is allowed to dry on the paper

water

Water soaks up the paper

Chromatography is used to separate dyes.

Whodunnit?

Forensic scientists help the police to solve crimes by examining the scene of a crime and analysing anything unusual.

They can analyse blood, fibres of clothing, hair, skin, paint that might have been scratched from a car – anything that is found.

Chromatography is a useful method for forensic scientists. By analysing the ink used to write a forged document, they can match it with ink from suspects' pens.

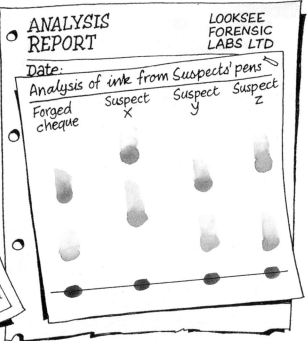

Who wrote the cheque?

Identifying common chemicals

You can analyse some things yourself.

- A gas that explodes with a squeaky pop when lit is *hydrogen*.
- A gas that makes lime water go cloudy when bubbled through it is *carbon dioxide*.
- A gas that makes a glowing spill light up again is *oxygen*.
- A gas that bleaches colours is *chlorine*.
- Pure substances have a fixed **melting point** which can be measured. Substances that are not pure melt over a range of temperatures. If you melt a solid and compare its melting point with known substances in a book of data, you can work out what it is.

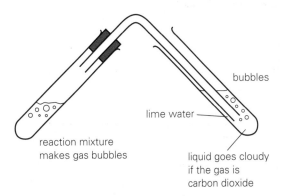

Testing for carbon dioxide.

QUESTIONS

1. Why might you have a blood test?
2. How could you find out what food colours are used in different sweets?
3. Why would a firm manufacturing make-up analyse their lipsticks?
4. How could you tell if a sample of ice is made from pure water or not?

KEY IDEAS

Chromatogaphy is a way of separating coloured materials.

Analysis is how chemists find out what a substance is made of.

1.6 Too small to see

How are bricks and football players like atoms and molecules?

A builder can't build a new house without knowing what bricks to use and how to fit them together. A good football team only plays well when everyone knows the strengths and weaknesses of each player. Why do you need to know about atoms and molecules?

Chemists can make useful materials only if they know what it's like inside the things they're reacting.

Dalton's study of particles was the start of what chemists call 'atomic theory'.

Particles

Everything is made of tiny **particles**. The Greeks first thought of this idea 3000 years ago. However, these particles are too small to see. It wasn't until about 1800 that chemists did experiments that started to prove the idea. John Dalton called these particles **atoms**.

How do you know where the scent is?

How do we know that particles exist?

When you go into your local department store, you can tell where the perfume counter is with your eyes shut! Somehow, tiny particles of the perfume reach your nose.

When you dissolve one sweetener in your coffee, you only need one drop of coffee on your tongue to taste it. Bits of sweetener, too small to see, must have spread through the coffee.

These observations suggest scent and sweeteners are made of tiny particles.

Particles on the move

A Scottish scientist called Robert Brown first saw evidence for particles moving. He looked at water and grains of pollen under a microscope and saw the pollen move in a jerky way. He decided that the particles of water must be pushing the pollen about.

This effect is called **Brownian motion**. It's a bit like trying to stand still outside a football ground before a match. You get pushed about by the crowd around you.

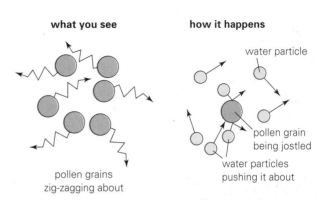

what you see

pollen grains zig-zagging about

how it happens

water particle

pollen grain being jostled

water particles pushing it about

How pollen grains get pushed about by water.

How quickly do particles move about?

You can soon smell the food round the house when you start cooking, so particles must move through the air quickly. If you leave a sugar lump in water, it takes quite a while for the sugar to dissolve. Particles travel more slowly through liquids than gases.

Ah ... I smell breakfast!

QUESTIONS

1. Who first thought that things were made of particles?

2. What evidence suggests that particles:
   a are small
   b move about all the time?

3. What did Robert Brown discover?

4.

   The diagram shows some sugar particles in a sugar lump you've just put in your tea. You go away and leave the mug. Draw a similar diagram to show where the particles might be 5 minutes later.

KEY IDEAS

All substances are made of particles, too small to see.

Particles move about all the time.

They move more quickly in gases than liquids.

1.7 *Crunchy, runny or breezy?*

When it's very cold, ponds and even the sea can freeze. You also turn water to steam when you boil it. How can water be a solid, a liquid and a gas ?

You can turn most things into **solids** if you get them cold enough. If you heat them up, sooner or later they will turn into **liquids**, and then **gases**.

Solids, liquids and gases are called the three **states of matter**.

The sea can freeze in winter.

Hot liquid rock (lava) runs down a volcano.

What is special about solids, liquids and gases?

Ice, rock, steel and paper are all solids. Solids are lumpy and have their own shapes, though they might bend, like paper. Most solids are hard. You can't squash solids, unless they have holes in them like a sponge.

Liquids are runny. You can pour them from one container to another. A litre of milk can be any shape – in a bottle or flat all over the floor! You can't squeeze liquids together easily. Don't squash your hot water bottle before the top is on, otherwise …

Steam is a gas. When you boil just a few drops of water, the steam gets everywhere. Gases can fill any space just as steam fills the kitchen. Most gases are very light and you can see through them. They are transparent. You can squash gases.

Solids, liquids and gases have different properties.

14

Why are solids solid, liquids runny and gases shapeless?

The particles in solids are *close together*, like a carefully loaded box of apples. Most solids therefore can't be squashed easily. They are stuck together by *strong forces*, so they keep their shape and don't fall apart. The particles are arranged in a *regular* way, so some solids are crystals.

solid

Liquids have particles that are *closely packed* like solids, so they can't be squashed, but they are *randomly arranged*. The particles *move about* all the time, so liquids are runny.

liquid

Gas particles behave like the balls in a lottery machine. They are a *long way apart*, so gases are light for their size and can be squashed. The particles *move quickly* and have only *weak forces* between them. Gases can therefore easily mix and fill the spaces they are put in.

gas

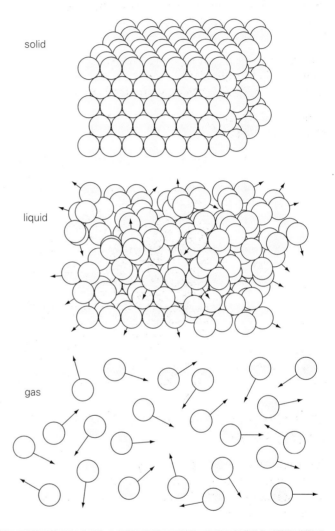

QUESTIONS

1 a What substance can be turned into ice and steam?

  b How can you cause these changes?

2 Draw a labelled picture to show the different properties of ice, water and steam.

3 Why can you pour liquids but not solids?

4 Why are gases much lighter than liquids?

5 Draw diagrams to show the particles in:

  a a lump of iron

  b fruit juice

  c the air in a balloon.

KEY IDEAS

Things can be solids, liquids or gases, the three states of matter.

The particles inside them are arranged in different ways.

1.8 Particles on the move!

**What happens inside substances when they get hot, melt or boil?
How can a substance travel through air or water?**

The idea of particles helps you to understand what is going on.

Heating and cooling

When you heat up things, they get bigger – they **expand**. The liquid in a thermometer expands and moves up the tube if the thermometer is put in a hotter place.

As you heat particles, they gain energy and move about more. The more they move, the more space they need, so the substance gets bigger. As they cool, the particles move less and the substance takes up less space – it **contracts**.

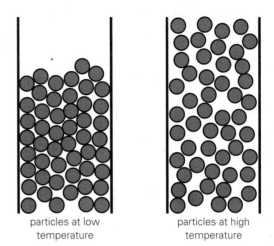

particles at low temperature

particles at high temperature

The gaps between particles in the thermometer get bigger as it gets hotter.

Melting and boiling

Chemists describe melting and boiling as **changes of state**.

The diagram shows what happens to particles in a solid like ice, as it gets hotter.

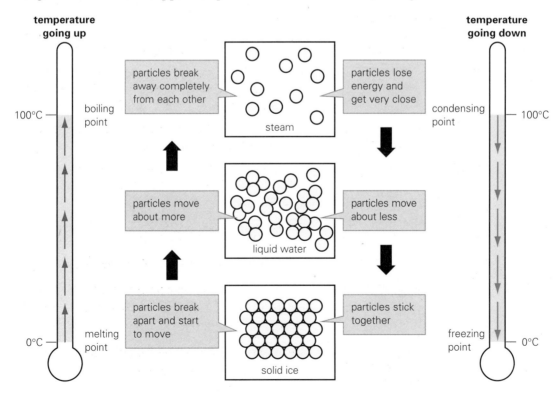

Changes in temperature cause changes of state.

Particles and gases

Gases can be squeezed together, because of the large gaps between the particles. When you pump air into a tyre, the pressure goes up. Pressure is caused by the air particles bumping into the sides of the tyre. The more particles you can squeeze in, then the more collisions you get with the sides. So the pressure goes up.

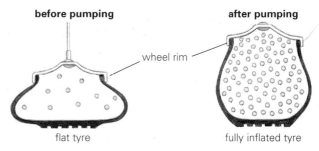

Pumping up a tyre increases the air pressure inside.

Particles and movement

When a coloured crystal is placed in some water, the colour gradually spreads though the water. The particles are moving all the time, so they become evenly mixed. This sort of mixing is called **diffusion**. Diffusion takes place more quickly in gases than in liquids, because the particles are moving faster.

QUESTIONS

1   Explain why a metal girder bridge is a tiny bit shorter in the winter compared with the summer.

2   The melting point of aluminium is 660°C, and its boiling point is 2470°C.

   a Describe what you will see happen to aluminium as it is heated from 600°C to 2500°C.

   b Draw diagrams to show what happens to the particles inside aluminium when the temperature goes down from 700°C to 600°C.

3   Explain how the air particles inside a balloon keep the balloon blown up.

4   What is diffusion? Explain how the scent from your deodorant spreads through the changing rooms.

KEY IDEAS

As things get hotter, the particles gain energy.

Melting, boiling, expanding and diffusion can all be explained by thinking about what happens to particles.

Pressure is caused by particles colliding with the walls of a container.

2.1 *Changing things*

A mixture of powders, a lighted match ... and a spectacular firework display! How do you know what will happen when you mix and heat things?

Chemists can change materials into different ones. Plants can become medicines, oil can be turned to plastics and mixtures of powders can cause explosions.

Physical changes are all around us.

Heating and cooling

You already know that materials can melt or boil when you heat them up. When you cool them down again, you get back to where you started. Ice in the Arctic can melt to water in the ocean and then evaporate into the air. Water in the air can turn back into liquid dew. This is called **condensation**. The dew may freeze on a cold night.

Melting and boiling, and the opposite processes of freezing and condensing, are examples of **physical changes**. Even dissolving is a physical change. You can still taste the salt when it is dissolved in water. You can then get it back by evaporating the water away. Physical changes can be reversed easily and no new substances get made.

No going back

What happens when you cook carrots, bake a cake or drive a car? You can't uncook the carrots or the cake! You can't reverse the car along the road and get back the petrol you used! Neither can you get a firework back by putting the stars and crackles into the tube again!

These changes are called **chemical changes** or **reactions**. Most chemical changes can't be reversed.

fuels burn to produce energy

the gun goes bang

the cake has been cooked

the cement sets to give a hard driveway

Chemical changes are at work all the time.

What happens in a chemical reaction?

You are an example of an amazing set of chemical reactions – a sort of walking chemical factory. You eat chips, burgers, apples and biscuits, and hundreds of other foods. You also drink liquids and breathe in air. You then turn these ingredients into blood, bones, nerves and skin – completely *new* chemicals.

In a chemical reaction, some substances are changed into *new* substances.

The body is a human chemical factory.

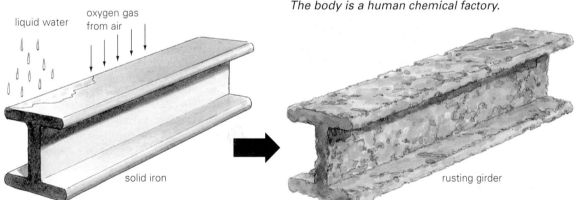

Iron rusting is a chemical reaction.

QUESTIONS

1   Write down three changes that might happen when you heat a substance.

2 a Draw a table with the headings: **Physical changes** and **Chemical changes**. Put the following in the correct columns: freezing water, burning petrol, dissolving sugar, eating food, boiling water, steam condensing on a cold window.

   b Think of two more changes you can add to each column.

3   Explain why the human body is like a chemical factory.

2.2 Chemical magic?

How can you change one substance into another? Is it a kind of magic?

Hundreds of years ago the chemists, called alchemists, were a bit like magicians. They had two main ambitions. One was to turn lead into gold, and the other was to make a potion called the 'elixir of life'. This would cure all disease and make people live for ever! Needless to say, they didn't succeed!

An alchemist at work in the Middle Ages.

Magicians or chemists?

Today you still can't turn lead into gold in a chemical reaction. You might see a conjurer *trick* you into thinking he can do magical things. He might turn water into wine or pull a rabbit from a hat, but you know this doesn't really happen.

Chemistry is not magic, but chemists can do some amazing things. They can turn rocks into metals like copper and iron. Sand can be turned into glass, or into silicon chips to make computers.

These flares are produced by a chemical reaction that makes light.

Heat and light

Military and distress flares can be made from magnesium. If you heat up a piece of magnesium, it soon bursts into a blinding white flame. It reacts with oxygen in the air to make a substance called magnesium oxide.

Lots of other reactions also make heat or light.

The magnesium oxide produced in a distress flare is very different from the starting materials. If you heat up magnesium oxide or cool it down, you can't get the magnesium or oxygen back again. Lots of energy is produced in the reaction: heat, light and even some crackles of sound. You can write the change down in a special way:

magnesium + oxygen → magnesium oxide

This is called a word equation. Magnesium and oxygen, the things that react, are called the **reactants**. The arrow shows what substance the reactants turn into. The magnesium oxide is the **product**.

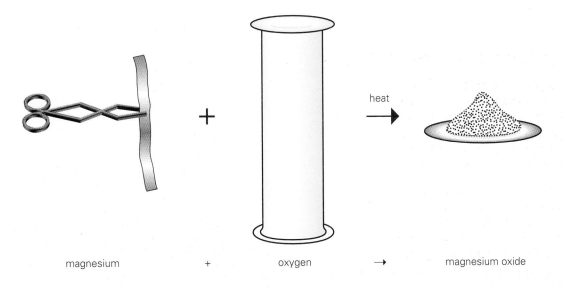

magnesium   +   oxygen   →   magnesium oxide

How to get a white powder from some metal ribbon and gas!

QUESTIONS

1 a What do you call the 'chemists' of the middle ages?

b What two things did they want to do?

2 a Describe what happens when magnesium and oxygen react.

b How do you know a chemical reaction has happened?

3 How do you know the following are reactions?

a Gas burning in a gas fire.

b Mixing sand, cement and water to make concrete.

2.3 *All sorts of reactions*

Chemicals behave a bit like us – they can find partners, break up again, and compete with each other for something they want.

Burning reactions

Burning is an important reaction. Fuels are burnt to give us energy, to drive our cars and heat our homes. Waste is destroyed in bonfires and incinerators.

When you burn anything, it reacts with oxygen in the air. If oxygen is added, the substance ought to get heavier. So why are you just left with a pile of ash after a bonfire?

A chemist called Lavoisier investigated this and managed to trap everything produced in a reaction. He found that the total weight did go up. It was just that some of the things made were gases, which escaped into the air.

For example, coal is mainly the chemical substance called carbon. It burns in air to make carbon dioxide, which is a gas. The gas escapes into the air and not much is left behind.

Burning is sometimes called **combustion**.

What happens when things burn?

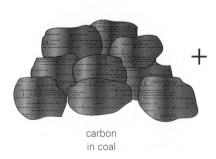 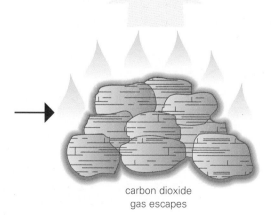

| carbon
in coal | + | oxygen
in air | → | carbon dioxide
gas escapes |

Coal burning is a chemical reaction.

Reacting with oxygen

Lots of materials react with air, but they don't burn. Iron rusts into iron oxide, and aluminium gets a white coating of aluminium oxide on it. All reactions in which oxygen is added to another substance are called **oxidation** reactions.

Oxygen from the air causes lots of other changes: a freshly cut apple gradually turns brown and cut potatoes go black in the air.

Breaking reactions

When chemicals are heated, they don't always react with oxygen. Some of them just break up into smaller pieces.

When you heat green copper ore, called malachite, it turns into a black powder and a gas is produced. The gas turns lime water milky, so it is carbon dioxide.

The malachite has broken down into other chemicals: it has **decomposed**. The equation for this change is:

copper carbonate (green solid) → copper oxide (black solid) + carbon dioxide (gas)

This reaction is an example of **thermal decomposition** (*thermal* means heat is used, *decomposition* means something breaks into smaller bits).

Peeled apples react with oxygen.

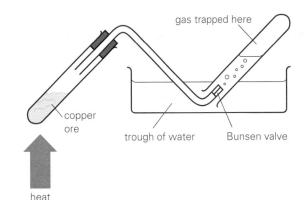

gas trapped here

copper ore

trough of water   Bunsen valve

heat

You can heat copper ore and trap the products.

QUESTIONS

1 What does coal react with when it burns?

2 What is **a** combustion and **b** oxidation?

3 How are oxidation and combustion similar to each other?

4 When you heat chalk, it turns to a white powder and loses weight. You suspect carbon dioxide gas is formed. Describe how you would try to prove this idea.

KEY IDEAS

Combustion and oxidation are both reactions with oxygen.

When heated, some substances decompose.

2.4 *How simple can you get?*

Did you know that, with about a hundred ingredients, you can make any substance in the world?

These special ingredients are called **elements**. However hard you try, you can't split these elements into other substances. They are the simplest substances you can get and are made from just one type of particle – an atom. The atoms of one element are different from the atoms of other elements.

Elements are sometimes called the *building bricks* of chemistry. A chemist can make *any* substance by putting the right amounts and types of atoms together.

Just under a hundred elements make everything on the Earth.

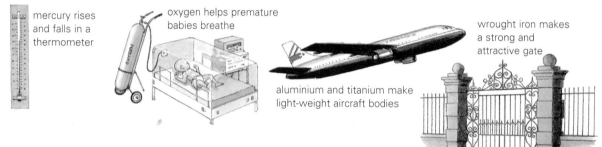

mercury rises and falls in a thermometer

oxygen helps premature babies breathe

aluminium and titanium make light-weight aircraft bodies

wrought iron makes a strong and attractive gate

Most of the elements are solid metals like zinc, copper, iron, silver and gold. Mercury is also an element and a metal, but it is a liquid. About 20 elements are not metals. These include gases like oxygen, nitrogen and hydrogen and solids like sulphur and carbon.

Some elements at work.

More complicated materials

Elements have lots of uses, but most of the chemicals around us are more complicated. Two or more atoms of different elements can join together to make a **compound**. Compounds are different from the elements of which they are made.

For example, water is a liquid compound made from hydrogen and oxygen. It is essential for life and is used to cool fires. Hydrogen and oxygen, on the other hand, are both gases, which would not put out fires. In fact, a mixture of them will explode if you put a match to it!

Hydrogen was used to fill airships – until disaster struck.

Firefighters use water to drench a fire.

Atoms and molecules

When two or more atoms join together you get another sort of particle, called a **molecule**. Some elements exist naturally as molecules. Oxygen molecules in the air are made of two atoms of oxygen. Nitrogen molecules are made of two atoms of nitrogen. Air is a mixture of mainly nitrogen and oxygen molecules.

Lots of compounds are made up from molecules. Carbon dioxide has molecules made from one carbon atom and two oxygen atoms. A water molecule consists of two hydrogen atoms and one oxygen atom.

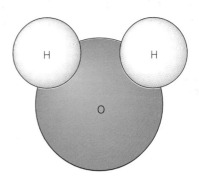

A molecule of water.

QUESTIONS

1 Write down the names of ten elements on these two pages.

2 What is special about an element?

3 What are the differences between atoms and molecules?

4 Look at the diagrams of atoms and molecules. Which diagrams show: **i** elements **ii** compounds **iii** single atoms **iv** molecules?
Explain how you decided.

a

b

c

d
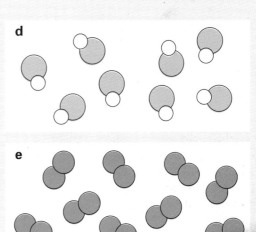

e

f
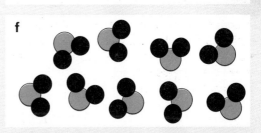

2.5 *The chemist's code*

***What does H₂O stand for? Why is iron Fe?
What are chemical equations? Why have
a special code?***

Chemical reactions can be pretty complicated, so
there is a special code to help you to understand
them. Every chemical element has its own **symbol**.
The same symbols are used wherever you go in the
world, so it's like an international language.

Symbols for elements

There is a symbol of just one or two letters for every
element. The letter H stands for one atom of
hydrogen and O for an atom of oxygen.

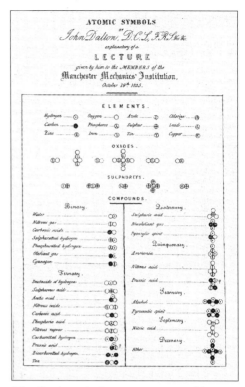

*The first symbols were suggested by
John Dalton, nearly 200 years ago.*

Some symbols are easy
to remember:

Element	Symbol
carbon	C
sulphur	S
nitrogen	N
phosphorus	P
iodine	I

Others aren't too bad;
they have two letters:

Element	Symbol
silicon	Si
calcium	Ca
bromine	Br
neon	Ne
krypton	Kr

A few more at least start
with the right letter:

Element	Symbol
zinc	Zn
copper	Cu
chlorine	Cl
magnesium	Mg

But some are very hard
to understand!

Element	Symbol
sodium	Na
iron	Fe
potassium	K
silver	Ag
gold	Au
mercury	Hg

*The symbol for silver is Ag.
It comes from the Latin word,
argentum, meaning 'shining'.*

All of the elements with odd symbols have been
known about for a long time. The symbols come from
Latin words that were used by chemists. For example,
the element potassium was first called kalium, which
meant 'woodash'. Potassium compounds were found
in the ashes of woodfires. Sodium was called natrium.
It got named sodium after an arabic word, soda. Soda
means 'splitting headache' and sodium compounds
were supposed to get rid of it!

What is a formula?

A molecule of oxygen has two atoms in it. So you can write its **formula** as O_2. The formula for water is H_2O, because a water molecule contains two hydrogen atoms and one oxygen atom. A formula tells you exactly the number of each atom in a molecule.

Equations

As you know, carbon will burn in oxygen – a solid combines with a gas to give off heat. Another gas, carbon dioxide, is formed. This is an example of a chemical reaction – when one set of substances re-arrange their atoms and end up in a different combination. You can write a word equation to show what happens:

carbon + oxygen → carbon dioxide

This tells you in a quick way that carbon and oxygen react together, and make carbon dioxide.

You can turn a word equation into a symbol equation by replacing each word with a symbol or formula.

carbon = C, oxygen = O_2, carbon dioxide = CO_2.

So the equation becomes:

$C + O_2 \rightarrow CO_2$

Word equations and symbol equations are both types of **chemical equations**.

methane CH_4
(natural gas)

ammonia NH_3

hydrogen chloride HCl

Some common molecules and their formulas.

QUESTIONS

1 Write out the names and symbols of all the elements on these two pages.

2 The formula of water is H_2O. What does this tell you?

3 The formula of a molecule in petrol is C_8H_{18}. Methane, CH_4, also contains C and H atoms. What makes these two molecules different?

2.6 What's in an atom?

You can't see atoms, so how do you know what they look like? Can you split them up?
What are they like inside?

Until a hundred years ago, chemists thought atoms were solid, like snooker balls. Then some chemists fired tiny particles at a thin piece of gold. Most of the particles went right through the gold without leaving a hole! A few bounced back. This was like throwing bricks at a wall and seeing most of them pass right through! Chemists decided that this meant the atoms of gold had lots of space inside them (like holes in the wall).

The most powerful microscope only lets you see the position of atoms on the surface of a metal.

Would you expect to throw stones through this wall?

Atomic particles

Atoms are made out of *three* smaller particles. **Protons** and **neutrons** are quite heavy and are found in a **nucleus** at the centre of the atom. **Electrons** are much smaller and lighter, and whizz around the nucleus. They form a 'cloud' around the nucleus. Protons and electrons carry an electrical charge, neutrons don't.

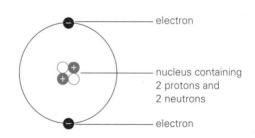

electron

nucleus containing 2 protons and 2 neutrons

electron

This helium atom has two protons, two neutrons and two electrons.

If an atom was the size of this stadium, the nucleus would be a marble at the centre!

Atomic particles			
Particle	**Where is it?**	**Mass**	**Electrical charge**
proton	in the nucleus	1 atomic unit	+1
neutron	in the nucleus	1 atomic unit	0
electron	in the space around the nucleus	very small, about $\frac{1}{1840}$ of an atomic unit	−1

What makes an atom of each element?

Every element has an **atomic number**. Hydrogen, the simplest element, has an atomic number of 1. The atomic number tells you how many protons there are in the atom.

Atoms are neutral – they have zero electrical charge. This means the number of electrons balances the number of protons. So the number of electrons is also given by the atomic number.

The mass number

The mass or weight of an atom is nearly all due to the protons and neutrons in the middle. The **mass number** tells you the total number of protons *and* neutrons in an atom.

The mass number of oxygen is 16. It has 8 protons (its atomic number is 8). So it has 16 – 8 = 8 neutrons.

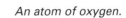

An atom of oxygen.

Name	Symbol	Atomic number	Number of electrons	Number of neutrons	Mass number
hydrogen	H		1	0	1
helium	He	2	2	2	4
lithium	Li	3	3	4	7
beryllium	Be	4	4	5	9
boron	B	5		6	11
carbon	C		6	6	12
nitrogen	N	7	7		14
oxygen	O	8	8	8	
fluorine	F		9	10	
neon	Ne		10		20

This table tells you what's inside the atoms of the first 10 elements.

QUESTIONS

1 What are the names of the particles in an atom?

2 What is the nucleus and what particles are in it?

3 What do the atomic number and mass number tell you about an element?

4 Copy the table above and fill in all the missing information.

2.7 More about atoms

Do electrons really travel round the nucleus like planets round the Sun?

Arranging the electrons

Are atoms really like mini solar systems?

Electrons travel round the nucleus along routes called **orbitals**, a bit like the path of a planet round the Sun. But an atom might be better compared with an onion. Each layer of the onion is like an **electron shell** of an atom. As you peel off each layer, you reach another shell.

an onion is made up of many layers

1st shell
2nd shell
3rd shell

an atom is made up of layers of electrons around the nucleus

Imagine cutting through an atom like an onion!

The electrons travel round the shells according to some simple rules:

- the first shell, nearest the nucleus, can hold 2 electrons
- the second and third shells can both hold 8 electrons each
- electrons try to get as close to the nucleus as possible – they fill the inner shells first.

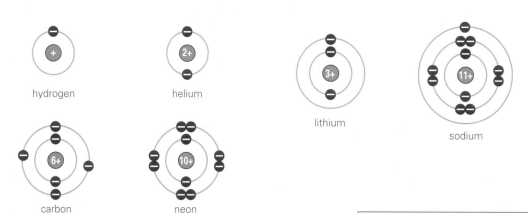

hydrogen

helium

lithium

sodium

carbon

neon

Atoms of each element have their own arrangement of electrons.

For example, lithium needs 3 electrons to balance the electrical charge in its nucleus. When the first shell has 2 electrons it is full, so the third electron goes into the second shell.

The arrangement of electrons in an atom is called an **electron configuration**. It can be written as a series of numbers. For example, the configuration for sodium is 2, 8, 1. This means it has 2 electrons in the first shell, close to the nucleus, then 8 in the next shell, and 1 in the third and outer shell.

Some electron configurations		
hydrogen	(H)	1
helium	(He)	2
lithium	(Li)	2, 1
oxygen	(O)	2, 6
sodium	(Na)	2, 8, 1
chlorine	(Cl)	2, 8, 7
potassium	(K)	2, 8, 8, 1

Atomic shorthand

Sometimes an atom of oxygen is written as $^{16}_{8}O$. This is a quick way of showing you the mass number (at the top) and the atomic number (at the bottom).

aluminium has 27 particles in its nucleus

27 − 13 = 14 so there are 14 neutrons

13 of them are protons

there must be 13 electrons to balance the charge of 13 protons

27
13 Al

Atomic shorthand tells you what's inside an atom.

Isotopes

You can tell one element from another by the differences in their atoms. All atoms of hydrogen have 1 proton. All carbon atoms have 6 protons. However, the numbers of neutrons *can* change.

There are three kinds of hydrogen atom, two kinds of carbon atom and two kinds of chlorine atom. Atoms of one element with different numbers of neutrons are called **isotopes**.

ordinary hydrogen   heavy hydrogen (deuterium)   very heavy hydrogen (tritium)

There are three isotopes of hydrogen.

Some common isotopes			
Element	Number of protons	Number of protons and neutrons	Number of neutrons
hydrogen	1	1	0
	1	2	1
	1	3	2
carbon	6	12	6
	6	14	8
chlorine	17	35	
	17	37	

QUESTIONS

1 Where are electrons found in atoms?

2 Fluorine has 9 electrons. How are they arranged?

3 Draw diagrams of the electron shells of
  a lithium **b** sodium
  c magnesium (12 electrons).

4 What do the following symbols stand for:
  a $^{1}_{1}H$ **b** $^{16}_{8}O$ **c** $^{37}_{17}Cl$

5 Copy and complete the table of isotopes above.

KEY IDEAS

Electrons are arranged in shells round the atom.

Isotopes are atoms of the same element with different numbers of neutrons.

SECTION A: QUESTIONS

1 Mrs Carter has a machine in her café which makes frothy hot chocolate. It mixes chocolate powder, milk, steam, sugar and water.

a Draw a table with the headings: **Ingredients** and **Solid, liquid or gas**.
Copy the five ingedients into the first column. State whether they are solid, liquid or gas in the second column.

b The packet of sugar says that it is 'pure'. What does this mean?

c When the sugar mixes with the water, a mixture is made. Is it a suspension or a solution?

d Not all the chocolate powder dissolves. Draw a diagram to describe how you can separate the bits that don't dissolve from the rest of the drink.

2 John broke a bottle containing salt. He swept up the salt and broken glass. Then he separated the salt from the glass by:
 i mixing the sweepings with water
 ii filtering it
 iii making salt crystals.

a State two ways in which John could make the salt dissolve as quickly as possible in stage **i**.

b What is separated from what in stage **ii**?

c How can salt crystals be separated from the solution in stage **iii**?

d John weighed the salt crystals that he finally got back. Look at the picture.

What mass of salt was lost?
Where is it likely to have disappeared to?

3 A pure substance was melted and then cooled down again. The temperature was taken each minute as it cooled down. The results were:

Time (min)	Temp. (°C)
0	65
1	49
2	45
3	45
4	45
5	45
6	44
7	43
8	40
9	38

a On a piece of graph paper, plot the temperature (up the left axis) against time (along the bottom axis).

b What do you think is happening to the substance at 45°C?

c How are the particles arranged in the substance at 65°C?

d How are the particles arranged in the substance at 44°C?

4 Tap water contains dissolved materials such as chlorine, which is added during water treatment.

a Where do you think the dissolved materials get into the water?

b Why is chlorine added to the water?

c Why can you *not* purify water by filtering it?

d Explain how you could get *pure* water from tap water. Draw a diagram to show what apparatus you would use.

5 Explain how you would carry out each of the following experiments. Draw diagrams of any apparatus you would use.

a obtain copper sulphate crystals from a solution of the crystals dissolved in water

b separate a mixture of the different food colourings in sweets

c obtain a sample of pure water from spring water.

6 Helium is a light gas used to fill weather balloons. It is kept under pressure in a metal cylinder until it is needed. Then a tap is turned on to let the gas out and fill the balloon.

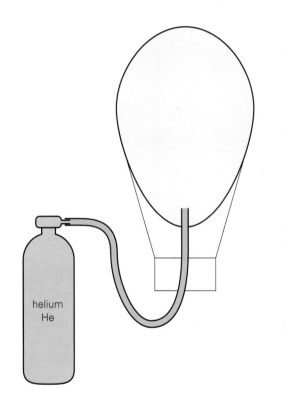

helium
He

a Draw two diagrams which show:
 i how the particles of helium are arranged under pressure in the cylinder
 ii how the particles are arranged once they are in the the balloon.
 Try to show the difference between **i** and **ii** as clearly as you can.

b As the balloon rises in the air, it gets colder. Draw a third diagram to show how the particles will be arranged in the balloon once it gets colder.

7 A family is planning a walking and camping holiday. They buy a number of new things for the trip. Look at the items in the catalogue.

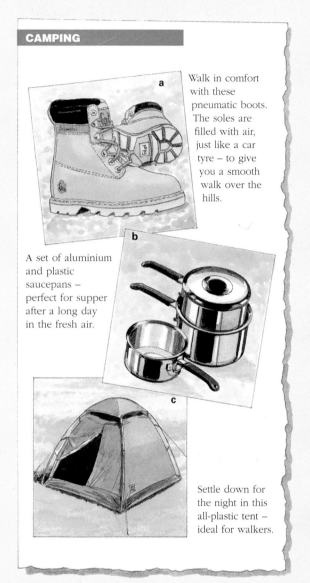

CAMPING

a Walk in comfort with these pneumatic boots. The soles are filled with air, just like a car tyre – to give you a smooth walk over the hills.

b A set of aluminium and plastic saucepans – perfect for supper after a long day in the fresh air.

c Settle down for the night in this all-plastic tent – ideal for walkers.

a i What is special about the soles of the walking boots?
 ii Use your understanding of particles and pressure to explain how these soles work.

b i What two materials are used to make the saucepans?
 ii Why are these materials chosen?
 iii Which parts of the pans would you expect to be made of each material?

c i What materials are used to make the tent?
 ii What properties of these materials make them suitable for a tent carried by walkers?

3.1 *Chemical families*

If you could predict the winning numbers in the lottery, you could be rich! But it is just a game of chance – the lucky players win.

In chemistry, you can make predictions that *can* come true. You might predict the result of a race – by knowing which athletes are racing and how well they have been running lately.

Chemists can predict what will happen in a reaction, by knowing about the chemicals they are reacting.

The top-form athlete wins the race.

Apparatus used by Lavoisier to investigate the elements.

Looking for patterns

Elements are the basic ingredients of reactions. They have been grouped in all sorts of ways. In 1790, a French chemist called Lavoisier divided the things known then as 'elements' into four groups:

- gas-like 'elements' such as oxygen, nitrogen, light and heat
- acid-making elements like sulphur, chlorine, carbon and phosphorus
- metals such as silver, cobalt, copper, tin, lead and zinc
- earthy elements like lime, barium oxide, silicon oxide.

Lavoisier couldn't split up the last group, though we can today. The elements in each of his groups behaved in similar ways. He had started the idea of chemical families.

Special types of atoms

After Dalton put forward his theory of atoms, scientists tried to look for patterns in the elements they knew. A German named Döbereiner put elements into threes called *triads*. Each element in a triad reacted in the same sort of way and the atomic masses made a pattern. The atomic mass of one was about half way between the other two.

In 1860, the British chemist Sir John Newlands arranged elements in order of their atomic masses. He found that every eighth element was a bit like the one eight elements before it. He called this his *Law of Octaves*.

Unfortunately, this only worked for the first 16 elements!

Many chemists thought that Newlands' ideas were ridiculous, but he was close to the truth. The elements *do* make repeating patterns, a bit like those on a roll of wallpaper.

Döbereiner's triads			
Element	Atomic mass	Element	Atomic mass
calcium	40	chlorine	35
strontium	88	bromine	80
barium	137	iodine	127

lithium
beryllium
boron
carbon
nitrogen
oxygen
fluorine
neon
sodium
magnesium
aluminium
silicon
phosphorus
sulphur
chlorine
argon
potassium
calcium

Elements make repeating patterns.

QUESTIONS

1 How did Lavoisier group his elements together?

2 Give an example of one of Döbereiner's triads and say what is special about it.

3 As a chemist today, say what you think is wrong with Lavoisier's grouping of:

   a gas-like elements

   b earthy elements.

3.2 *The periodic table*

There are over 100 different elements – is there any way of sorting them all out?

Visit your local record store and what do you see? The records, cassettes and CDs are all set out under headings: 'Chart', 'Dance', 'Jazz', 'Pop', 'Country and Western', and so on. Chemists do the same thing with elements.

The first chemist to manage to sort out the elements in the same sort of sensible way was the Russian, Dmitri Mendeléev.

A well-classified collection!

Mendeléev's predictions

Mendeléev put the elements in order of their atomic masses. He set them out just like you might lay out the suits from a pack of playing cards. When he got to an element like one he had met before, he started a new row. He ended up with families of similar elements in columns.

1 Sort the cards in each suit into order (ace, 2, 3 ... Jack, Queen, King).

2 Put the four suits together in one pile.

3 Deal the cards in rows, starting with an ace on the left.

4 When you get to the ace of another suit, start a new row.

The joker, like hydrogen, doesn't fit in easily.

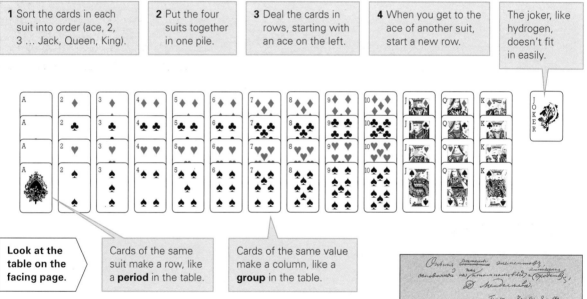

Look at the table on the facing page.

Cards of the same suit make a row, like a **period** in the table.

Cards of the same value make a column, like a **group** in the table.

Columns of cards are like Mendeléev's families of elements.

Not all the elements had been discovered when Mendeléev had his ideas. He was clever enough to leave gaps for them in his 'families' and predict what they would be like. All his gaps have now been filled.

Mendeléev's arrangement of the elements is now called the **periodic table**.

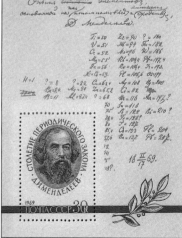

This Russian stamp shows Dmitri Mendeléev and his periodic table.

The modern periodic table

The table that you use today may look complicated, but it is based on some simple ideas.

The elements are put in order of their atomic number.

Elements are put in columns or **groups**. The groups are numbered 1 to 8. This tells you how many electrons are in the outside electron shell of each atom.

Elements are put in rows or **periods**.

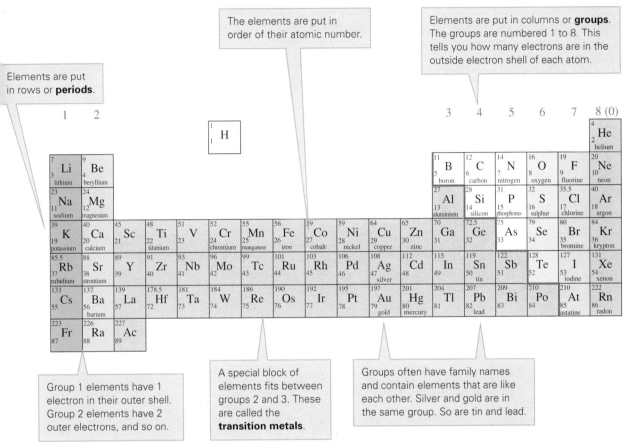

Group 1 elements have 1 electron in their outer shell. Group 2 elements have 2 outer electrons, and so on.

A special block of elements fits between groups 2 and 3. These are called the **transition metals**.

Groups often have family names and contain elements that are like each other. Silver and gold are in the same group. So are tin and lead.

QUESTIONS

1 What did Mendeléev do with the elements?

2 Not all the elements had been discovered when Mendeléev did his work.

a What did he do about it?

b What happened when they were discovered?

3 Look at the diagram of the periodic table to help you answer:

a How many elements are in the second period?

b What are the names of elements in group 4?

c Which group is oxygen in?

4 Copper, silver and gold are all in the same group of the periodic table. How are these elements similar to each other?

KEY IDEAS

The periodic table is a powerful way of grouping elements.

It is divided into groups and periods.

3.3 Marvellous metals

Metals are really important everyday materials, used to make many things from planes to pins. So what makes them so special?

A selection of metal gadgets from your home.

Over 80 elements are **metals**. How does a metal like iron or copper compare with a non-metal like oxygen?

The different properties of metals make them useful.

Steel is used to reinforce concrete.

Property of metal	Uses
strong, not easily snapped	girders for bridges reinforcing concrete
shiny when clean	jewellery
hard to melt or boil, high melting and boiling points (mercury is the only liquid metal)	inside of stoves, and cookers
malleable (can be pressed into shapes)	car bodies
ductile (can be made into wires)	electrical cables
good **conductors** of electricity and heat	electrical cables, radiators, saucepans
high density (even small bits are heavy)	weights for scales
sonorous ('clang' when hit)	bells and chimes

Not so marvellous!

Not all properties of metals are useful. Some lose their shine when they react with oxygen in the air. They form oxides. Rust is iron oxide.

Non-metals are different

Non-metals can be solids, liquids or gases. Most don't conduct heat or electricity. If solid, they crack or break easily: they are brittle. They usually melt and boil at low temperatures. They aren't strong, malleable, ductile or sonorous.

What makes a metal?

Metal atoms are joined in a particular way that makes them strong and malleable. They pack together very closely in a **giant structure**. Metals are heavy because their atoms are so close together. Strong forces hold the atoms together.

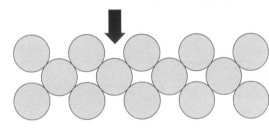

Atoms in metals are closely packed.

When you hammer a metal, the atoms slide round each other, making the metal malleable.

When you hit a metal with a hammer the atoms slide over each other and the metal becomes flatter.

The electrons in the outer shells of the atoms are able to move round the giant structure. So metals conduct electricity.

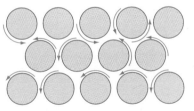

Electrons can carry electricity through metal.

QUESTIONS

1 What type of materials are strong, heavy and conduct heat?

2 Draw a poster to show six different uses of metals. For each use, explain *why* a metal is used for the job.

3 Why is copper used to make electrical cables and the bottoms of saucepans?

4 Design a table to show five differences between iron and oxygen.

5 Gold can be hammered into really thin pieces, called gold leaf. Draw a series of pictures to show what happens to the gold atoms as the lump of metal gets flatter.

KEY IDEAS

Metals have important properties that make them very useful.

Metals are made from closely packed giant structures of atoms.

3.4 *Peculiar metals*

What sort of metal floats on water or burns when wet? You expect metals to be tough and heavy, but one chemical family breaks all the rules!

Metals like cheese?

Lithium, sodium and potassium conduct electricity and heat like other metals. They look dull, but you can cut them as easily as cheese and inside they shine like silver. They soon tarnish as the oxygen in the air gets at them. This happens so quickly that these metals are kept in jars under oil. Sodium reacts with oxygen to make sodium oxide.

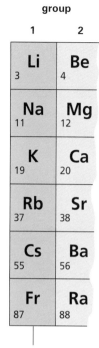

group

1	2
Li 3	Be 4
Na 11	Mg 12
K 19	Ca 20
Rb 37	Sr 38
Cs 55	Ba 56
Fr 87	Ra 88

Group 1 in the periodic table. the alkali metals

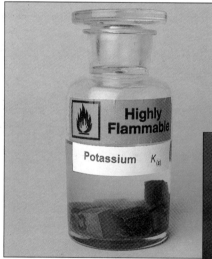

Potassium is kept under oil so air can't get at it.

Potassium reacts spectacularly with water.

Floating on water

You get an astonishing effect when you put a piece of potassium into water. The metal bursts into a lilac coloured flame, floats and dashes around like a speed boat, sizzling and crackling.

Soon, the metal disappears. The water now contains potassium hydroxide. This chemical is an *alkali*. You will find out more about alkalis in the next chapter.

Sodium melts and fizzes on water. Lithium reacts a bit more slowly, and it is possible to trap a gas bubbling from the metal. The gas burns with a squeaky pop, so it must be hydrogen.

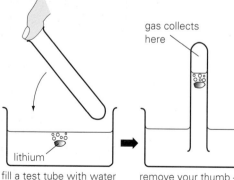

gas collects here

lithium

fill a test tube with water and place it over the lithium

remove your thumb – the lithium floats up the tube

Lithium produces a gas when it reacts with water.

The family name

This family is known as the **alkali metals**, because they make alkalis with water. You can write the reaction of sodium as:

sodium + water $\rightarrow$ sodium hydroxide + hydrogen

Following the trend

Sodium is more reactive than lithium. Potassium is more reactive than sodium. As you go *down* the group, the metals become *more* reactive. Chemists describe this as a **trend** down the group.

Compounds of the alkali metals

Alkali metals are so reactive that they make compounds very easily. The salt you shake on your chips is sodium chloride, made from sodium and chlorine. Sodium hydroxide, commonly called caustic soda, is used in oven and drain cleaners as it gets rid of grease. Potassium chloride is used in fertilisers because potassium helps plants to grow.

All of these compounds are white crystals that easily dissolve in water. These solids are made with strong bonds.

Sodium chloride adds flavour to food.

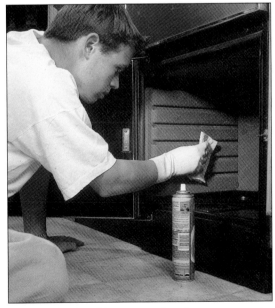

Sodium hydroxide makes cleaning ovens easier.

QUESTIONS

1   What properties of alkali metals make them unusual?

2   Describe what happens when potassium reacts with water.

3   Look at this data:

	Lithium	Sodium	Potassium
melting point(°C)	180	98	64
boiling point(°C)	1330	890	774

a What is the trend in melting points?

b Draw two bar charts showing the information in this table.

KEY IDEAS

The alkali metals are soft and very reactive.

They react with water to make hydrogen and alkalis.

41

3.5 Normal metals

Where can you find 'normal' metals in the periodic table?

The central section of the table contains well-known metals like iron, copper and zinc. These are called the transition metals.

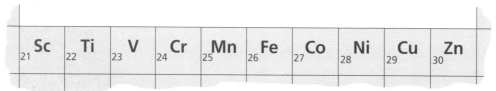

21 Sc	22 Ti	23 V	24 Cr	25 Mn	26 Fe	27 Co	28 Ni	29 Cu	30 Zn

Some transition elements in the periodic table.

Transition metals are good conductors of heat and electricity, and they are difficult to melt. The compounds that they make are often coloured. The colours of the stones you pick up on the beach are probably caused by transition metals. Iron makes rocks brown, and copper makes them green.

Comparing transition metals with sodium				
Property	Transition metals			Group 1 metal
	Iron	Copper	Cobalt	Sodium
melting point(°C)	1535	1083	1492	98
boiling point(°C)	3000	2595	2900	890
mass of 1 cm³ (g)	7.9	8.9	8.9	0.97
colour of compounds	brown or green	blue or green	pink or blue	white

Nickel for breakfast

Spread a piece of toast with margarine and you've used a transition metal in two ways.

Margarine is made by reacting liquid vegetable oil, like sunflower oil, with hydrogen. This makes the oil harder, but not too hard to spread. The metal nickel is added as the oil and hydrogen are mixed together. The nickel makes the other chemicals react together more quickly, though it doesn't join in the reaction itself. When something works in this way, like the nickel, it is called a **catalyst**.

Lots of transition metals are good catalysts. They save the margarine manufacturer time and money.

You have probably spread your margarine with a stainless steel knife. Stainless steel is a solid mixture of iron, nickel and chromium which doesn't go rusty when you do the washing up. Mixtures of different metals are called **alloys**.

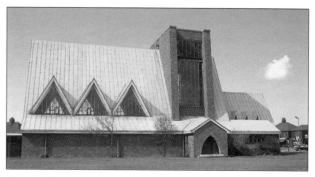

Copper forms green compounds when exposed to air.

Transition metals on toast!

42

Changing metals

Though iron is an easy transition metal to make, pure iron isn't used for many jobs. Usually, small amounts of other metals are added to make **steel** alloys, which are more useful.

Steel alloy	'Ingredients' as well as iron	Properties	Uses
mild steel	carbon	hard	car bodies
stainless steel	chromium, nickel	doesn't corrode	sinks, cutlery
tungsten steel	tungsten	very tough	tools and armour plate

Alloys are usually tougher than pure metals. The diagram helps to explain why.

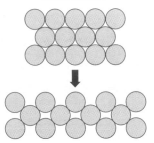

iron atoms are all the same size

they squash round each other easily when hit

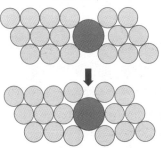

different sized atoms in the alloy

the atoms don't squash round so easily

QUESTIONS

1 Where can you find the transition metals in the periodic table?

2 Write down four properties of transition metals.

3 You pick up a green piece of rock. What metals might be inside it?

4 How is nickel used to help make margarine?

5 What is an alloy? Draw pictures to show the different uses of **a** mild steel, and **b** stainless steel.

3.6 *Useful poisons?*

*There is one group of elements that is deadly,
but we can't live without them!*

Imagine being in the trenches during the
First World War with no guns going off.
Instead, something silent and deadly creeps
across the battlefield towards you. It chokes
you and smells terrible. What can it be?
This is chemical warfare and you can smell
poisonous chlorine gas.

Chlorine is a heavy greenish-yellow gas
that you can see as well as smell. It's very
useful even though it's a poison. In *small*
amounts, it kills germs *without* killing you.
So it gets added to water in swimming
pools, and to your mains water supply, to
make sure you don't catch diseases.

You can even buy a form of chlorine at the
supermarket! Small amounts dissolve in
water to make bleach. Bleach kills germs
and takes the colour out of things. You
might put some down the toilet or sink to
make sure they are completely clean.

*Troops used gas masks to protect them from
poisonous gases.*

Hazardous chlorine.

Chlorine reacts

Chlorine is found in lots of substances. It
reacts with sodium to make sodium chloride
(salt), which you cook with. You can make
it react with other metals to make *chlorides*.
So iron and chlorine make iron chloride.

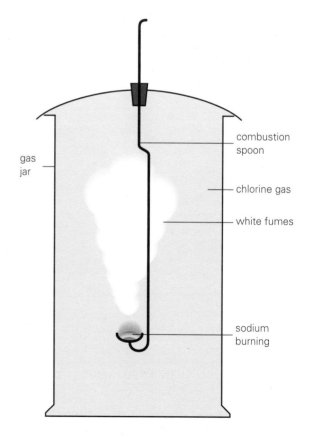

combustion
spoon

gas
jar

chlorine gas

white fumes

sodium
burning

Sodium reacts with chlorine.

A family of non-metals

Chlorine belongs to a family of elements in group 7 of the periodic table, called the **halogens**.

This word means *acid maker*, because all members of the family can react to make acids easily. You will find out more about acids in the next chapter. Chlorine and hydrogen make hydrogen chloride. This dissolves in water to make hydrochloric acid.

All members of the family are non-metals. They include bromine and iodine. As you go down this family, the elements get darker in colour and less reactive. This is the *opposite* to the pattern in group 1.

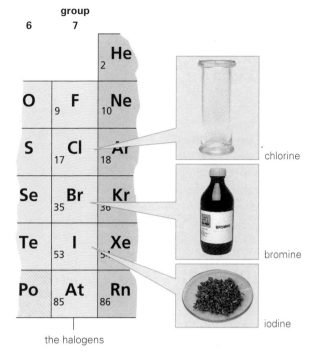

group
6   7

O	F₉	Ne₁₀	He₂
S	Cl₁₇	Ar₁₈	
Se₃₅	Br₃₅	Kr₃₆	
Te₅₃	I₅₃	Xe	
Po₈₅	At₈₅	Rn₈₆	

the halogens

chlorine

bromine

iodine

The halogen family is group 7 of the periodic table.

The table tells you some things about the halogens.

	Chlorine	Bromine	Iodine
What's it like?	green gas	brown liquid	purple solid
Boiling point (°C)	–35	59	184
Symbol	Cl	Br	I
Molecule	Cl_2	Br_2	I_2
Atomic number	17	35	53
Name in compounds	chloride	bromide	iodide
Compound with hydrogen	all colourless acid gases		
	hydrogen chloride	hydrogen bromide	hydrogen iodide
Compound with sodium	all white crystals		
	sodium chloride	sodium bromide	sodium iodide

QUESTIONS

1   Name a poisonous gas used in trench warfare.

2   What everyday uses does chlorine have?

3   Name two of the other elements in group 7 and write a sentence to describe each.

4   How do the elements change in their looks and reactions as you go down group 7?

KEY IDEAS

The halogens are non-metals in group 7 of the periodic table.

They become less reactive as you go down the group.

3.7 The halogens

Halogens are used everywhere – from the medicine cabinet to the photo album!

Acid making

In a chemical factory, you can burn chlorine in hydrogen. A gas called hydrogen chloride is formed. This is made of small HCl molecules. When you dissolve it in water, you get hydrochloric acid. This acid has lots of important uses. For instance, it helps to make PVC, an important plastic.

Bromine also reacts with hydrogen to make a gas, hydrogen bromide. This also makes an acid in water. Bromine doesn't react as quickly as chlorine. You can make a third acid gas from this chemical family, hydrogen iodide, as well.

Compounds with non-metals

Chlorine reacts with lots of other non-metals to make useful molecules. It makes antiseptics like TCP – the C in TCP stands for chlorine. Both chlorine and bromine are used for making medicines.

Compounds with metals

You can safely make compounds of chlorine in the laboratory yourself. There are two ways, as shown in the diagram.

Compounds of metals with the halogens are all solids with high melting points. Silver bromide is used to make photographic films and paper because it goes dark when exposed to light.

PVC in many shapes and colours.

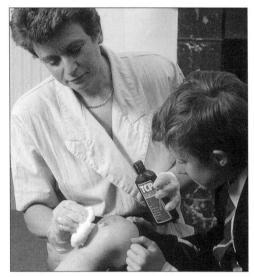
A graze is treated with antiseptic to kill germs.

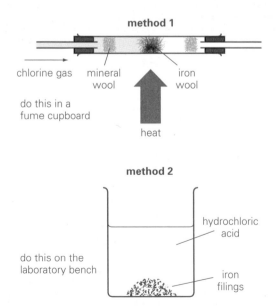

method 1

chlorine gas   mineral wool   iron wool

do this in a fume cupboard

heat

method 2

hydrochloric acid

do this on the laboratory bench

iron filings

Making iron chloride.

Where do you get bromine from?

Bromine is an unpleasant liquid, which doesn't occur naturally as an element. There are quite a lot of bromide compounds in the sea, though. If you bubble chlorine gas through sea water, the water goes brown. Chlorine displaces the bromine, because chlorine is more reactive than bromine.

chlorine + sodium bromide → sodium chloride + bromine
(in sea water) (brown)

Chlorine will also displace iodine from a solution of sodium iodide. However, you can't get chlorine out of chlorides using bromine or iodine, because they are less reactive than chlorine.

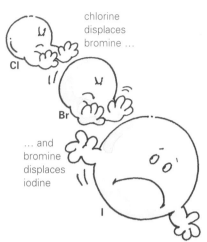

chlorine displaces bromine …

… and bromine displaces iodine

How important is iodine?

Iodine can be used as an antiseptic, because it kills germs in the same way as chlorine. You need to have small amounts of iodine in your diet, because it helps the thyroid gland in your neck to work properly.

There is a lot of iodine in sea weed.

This person has a goitre, a swelling in the neck, because his thyroid isn't working properly.

QUESTIONS

1 What acid gas can you make from chlorine?

2 Draw six pictures to show some uses of halogen compounds.

3 Describe how you would make zinc chloride in the laboratory.

4 a Would you expect bromine to react more strongly with sodium iodide solution or sodium chloride solution?

b Why?

c What new substances would be made in this reaction?

KEY IDEAS

The halogens make lots of useful compounds.

Chlorine displaces bromine from bromides and iodine from iodides.

Bromine displaces iodine from iodides.

3.8 *A noble family*

group

7	8 (0)
	$_2$ **He**
$_9$ **F**	$_{10}$ **Ne**
$_{17}$ **Cl**	$_{18}$ **Ar**
$_{35}$ **Br**	$_{36}$ **Kr**
$_{53}$ **I**	$_{54}$ **Xe**
$_{85}$ **At**	$_{86}$ **Rn**

Every family has a few unusual members,
but the periodic table has an unusual family!

There are all sorts of elements. All the metals are solids except liquid mercury. Gold doesn't tarnish like other metals, but stays shiny. Carbon has found its way into all the large molecules which make up living things. Most elements in the periodic table are useful because they react with other elements to form compounds, but the family in group 8 (0) is unique because it doesn't react.

The noble gases were fitted onto the end of the periodic table when they were discovered.

the noble gases

The bright lights of neon

Piccadilly Circus in London is famous for its neon lights.

The last group of elements in the periodic table are all gases. They glow brightly when electricity goes through them. You can see neon in action in coloured advertising lights.

These gases like neon are called the **noble gases**, because they don't like reacting with other elements. They are sometimes called **inert** gases, which means unreactive.

The noble gases had not been discovered when the periodic table was first thought about. Nobody knew they were there because they were so unreactive!

Bulbs and balloons

All the noble gases have lots of other uses. Helium is very light. It is lighter than air, so it is used to fill airships and weather balloons.

Argon is used to fill ordinary light bulbs. Inside the bulbs there is a thin metal wire, or filament, which glows white hot.

If the bulb contained any oxygen, the filament would burn and break, so unreactive argon is used. Xenon and krypton are used in photographic flashes for the same reason.

Helium is a safe and useful lightweight gas.

Why are the noble gases noble?

These gases are at the end of each row in the periodic table. The next element starts a new shell of electrons.

Helium has two electrons in its outside shell. Neon and argon have eight. These shells are full. Atoms like to have full shells, because this makes them stable. Noble gases are stable – they don't react with other atoms. They go round as single atoms.

helium (He)

neon (Ne)

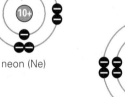

argon (Ar)

The electron shells are full in noble gas atoms.

QUESTIONS

1   What happens when electricity goes through neon?

2   Why is this group called the noble gases?

3   Draw a chart to show what these gases are used for.

4   What is special about noble gas atoms?

3.9 Chemical 'glue'

***How do you make atoms stick together?
You may think atoms are a bit like snooker
balls, but balls don't stick together when
they bump into each other!***

In chemical reactions, atoms bump into each other and
join together in new ways to make new materials.
However, you don't have to add glue to make sodium
react with chlorine. There must be a special way of
holding these atoms together.

*Atoms don't react like snooker balls,
otherwise everything around us would
break apart.*

Fatal attraction?

You can stick a balloon to the
ceiling by rubbing it. This charges it
up with *static electricity*. Extra tiny
electrons get rubbed onto the
balloon to make it *negatively
charged*. The balloon will then be
attracted to anywhere that is
positively charged.

The first bits of atoms that collide
with each other must be the outer
electrons. These electrons can
sometimes move from one atom to
another, a bit like those that were
rubbed onto the balloon.

This is what happens when sodium
reacts with chlorine. An electron
gets knocked off the outside of a
sodium atom.

The sodium atom now has a *positive*
charge, because it has *lost* a
negative electron.

Chlorine cannot lose electrons
easily, but it has the space for one
extra electron. It takes the electron
lost by sodium.

Chlorine now has 8 electrons round
its outer shell, which makes it full.
This extra electron gives the
chlorine atom a *negative* charge.

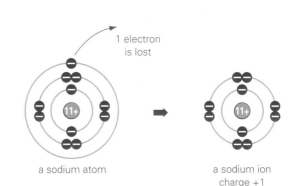

1 electron
is lost

a sodium atom

a sodium ion
charge +1
(8 electrons round outside)

Sodium loses an electron.

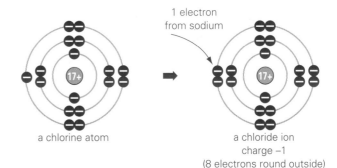

1 electron
from sodium

a chlorine atom

a chloride ion
charge −1
(8 electrons round outside)

Chlorine gains an electron.

Charged particles

Opposites attract!

The charged atoms are called **ions** and they attract each other. Lots of positive sodium ions are formed and they attract lots of negative chloride ions. (Remember, opposites attract!)

Salt is made of a giant structure of ions, held together by strong forces of attraction. This type of attraction between atoms is called **ionic bonding**. A **bond** is a chemical joint holding atoms together.

There are lots of ionic compounds formed between metals and non-metals. They have special properties.

Ionic compounds:

- have high melting points because of the strong bonds
- conduct electricity when they dissolve in water, because the charged ions can move about
- also conduct electricity when they are melted
- are crystals.

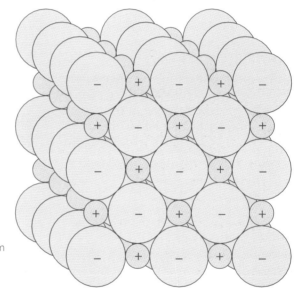

chloride ion

sodium ion

Large numbers of ions make up a complete crystal of sodium chloride.

QUESTIONS

1. How can you make a balloon stick to the ceiling?

2. What happens when a positive charge comes near to a negative one?

3. Draw a diagram of the electrons in:
   a a sodium atom
   b a sodium ion.
   What are the differences between the two?

4. Explain how chlorine uses the lost electron from sodium to make an ion.

KEY IDEAS

Metals like sodium form positive ions.

Non-metals like chlorine form negative ions.

Metals and non-metals join together to form ionic compounds.

3.10 *What holds water together?*

*What holds molecules together in water?
It's not solid like salt, so how do the hydrogen
and oxygen atoms stick together?*

Water is runny and it boils at only
100°C, so you must be able to break
apart some of its molecules quite easily.
There must be a strong force *inside* each
molecule, holding the hydrogen and
oxygen atoms together, but there can't
be much force *between* them.

strong forces between atoms
hold the molecules together

weak forces hold
the molecules close
to each other

Weak and strong forces hold water molecules together.

When you make a molecule like water,
electrons on the outside of the atoms get
shared. This is easy to see in the
simplest molecule you know about:
hydrogen. Two atoms of hydrogen join
to make a molecule, H_2.

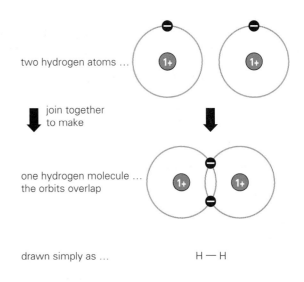

two hydrogen atoms ...

join together
to make

one hydrogen molecule ...
the orbits overlap

drawn simply as ...   H — H

Hydrogen atoms share electrons in a hydrogen molecule.

This type of joint between atoms is
called a **covalent bond**. It is
sometimes drawn as a line between
atoms. One line means that *two*
electrons are being shared between
two atoms.

Electrons are shared in lots of
substances made from non-metals.
Natural gas, methane, is made from
carbon and hydrogen. The methane
molecule, CH_4, is made from one
carbon atom and four hydrogen atoms.

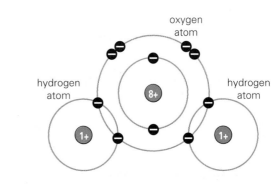

oxygen
atom

hydrogen
atom

hydrogen
atom

A water molecule has two covalent bonds.

What are covalent substances like?

Most substances that share electrons are like water, hydrogen and methane. They are usually gases or liquids (or solids that melt easily). They all have low melting and boiling points. There isn't much force holding their separate molecules together. They don't let electricity through because there aren't any spare electrons moving about.

Some common covalent substances				
Substance	Formula of molecule	Diagram of molecule	Melting point(°C)	Boiling point(°C)
iodine	I_2	I-I	114	183
hydrogen	H_2	H-H	−259	−252
sulphur	S_8	S-S-S-S-S-S-S-S	113	445
water	H_2O	H–O–H	0	100
ethanol	C_2H_5OH	H-C-C-O-H	−117	79
methane	CH_4	H-C-H	−182	−162

Comparing ionic and covalent substances

You can now look around you and work out how atoms are fixed together. Most soft, runny or gas-like things are joined with covalent bonds. Hard things that look like crystals are ionic.

some covalent materials

some ionic materials

chalk cliffs

iron ore

QUESTIONS

1 What is the name given to the type of bond that holds atoms in a water molecule together?

2 Draw a diagram of a hydrogen molecule, showing how electrons are shared.

3 Draw a bar chart that shows the melting points of five covalent substances.

4 Make a chart that shows:

a the structure of water and sodium chloride

b how their atoms are joined together.

KEY IDEAS

Non-metals are joined together by covalent bonds.

Electrons are shared in covalent bonds.

Substances with these bonds are often gases and liquids.

3.11 *Diamonds are for ever!*

***Diamonds are beautiful crystals.
They don't melt and they don't dissolve
in water. Why are they so special?***

Diamonds are smooth, hard and shiny. They are
one of the hardest substances and can only be cut
by other diamonds. The drills used to bore into the
ground to get oil are tipped with diamonds. So why
are diamonds so tough?

Diamonds are made from carbon atoms that
keep joining up together by strong covalent bonds.
One diamond crystal is made out of just one
giant structure, so it is really difficult to
break apart.

diamond

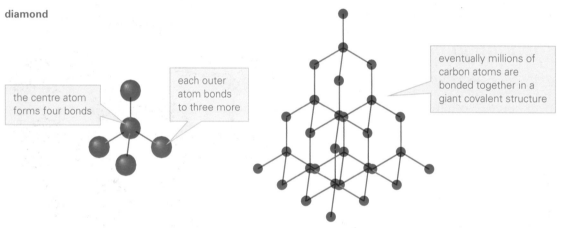

the centre atom
forms four bonds

each outer
atom bonds
to three more

eventually millions of
carbon atoms are
bonded together in a
giant covalent structure

How bonds make a diamond strong.

The same atoms that make diamonds are also in
your pencil! The 'lead' in your pencil is actually
graphite. Graphite is made of carbon atoms joined
in another way.

graphite

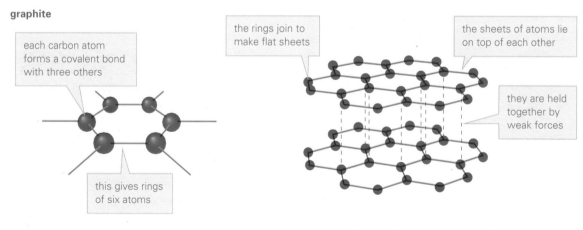

each carbon atom
forms a covalent bond
with three others

the rings join to
make flat sheets

the sheets of atoms lie
on top of each other

they are held
together by
weak forces

this gives rings
of six atoms

Layers of atoms in graphite.

54

Like diamond, graphite is difficult to melt. But graphite is soft – so soft that it rubs off the pencil onto your paper. This is because the layers in its giant structure can slide off easily. This property makes graphite a useful lubricant – you can spray it into door locks to loosen them when they get stiff.

Graphite is the only common non-metal to conduct electricity. This is because there are loose electrons between the layers of carbon atoms.

Graphite is soft, so rubs off onto paper.

Designer carbon

Chemists have recently made another type of carbon. This has atoms joined together in shapes like footballs called 'buckyballs'!

Could you become a millionaire by turning pencil lead into diamonds? It can be done, but it needs a lot of pressure to make the atoms change places, and the quality is not as good as natural diamonds. Diamonds good enough for drilling can be made in this way, but you wouldn't get them into the crown jewels!

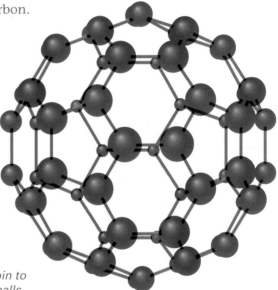

Carbon atoms can also join to form molecules like footballs.

QUESTIONS

1 What type of atoms are diamonds made from?

2 **a** Draw a diagram showing a few atoms in a diamond structure.

 b Explain why diamonds are so hard.

3 Why do we say a diamond has a giant structure?

4 What type of carbon would you use to:

 a help the moving parts of a machine move more smoothly

 b put on the tip of a crystal cutter? Explain your choices.

5 Why is graphite used in pencils?

6 Why is hydrogen a gas but carbon a solid, even though they are both non-metals?

KEY IDEAS

Carbon can exist as diamond and graphite.

Diamond is very hard and doesn't conduct electricity.

Graphite is soft and conducts electricity.

3.12 *Perfect predictions?*

What use is a periodic table? Can it help you to make scientific predictions?

The periodic table is like a chemical map. If you find where an element is on the map, you can say what the element must be like.

What does the map tell you?

Look at this periodic table. You can see some simple rules about where to find elements.

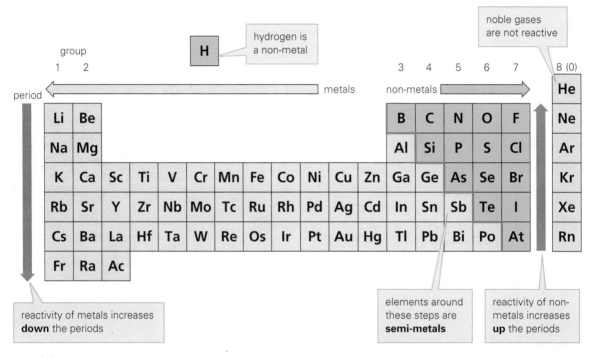

The periodic table is like a map.

Metals are on the left. Non-metals are on the right. The elements between metals and non-metals are called **semi-metals**. They behave a bit like metals. Silicon is used for the 'chips' in computers. It is a **semiconductor**, which means it conducts some electricity.

Computers contain silicon chips.

Making new substances

What if you want to make a new substance? You can make just the type of substance you want by reacting the right type of elements together.

- If you combine a *metal* with another *metal*, you get an alloy. For example, tin and copper make bronze.

- If you react a *metal* with a *non-metal*, you get an ionic compound. For example, sodium and chlorine make sodium chloride.

- If you react a *non-metal* with another *non-metal*, you get a covalent compound. For example, hydrogen and oxygen make water.

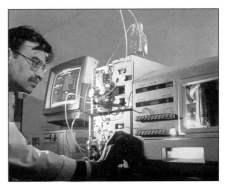

A chemist works on a new chemical.

Making ions

Ionic crystals are made from charged atoms. How do you know what charge will be on the atom? Metals have smaller numbers of electrons round their outer shells than non-metals. These are easily lost, so *metals form positive ions*.

- Metals in group 1 have 1 electron in the outer shell. They lose this to form ions with a charge of +1.

- Metals in group 2 have 2 outer electrons. They lose these to form ions with a charge of +2.

- Metals in group 3 have 3 outer electrons. They form +3 ions.

Non-metals like to gain electrons to fill their outer shells. *Non-metals form negative ions*.

- Elements in group 7 only need 1 more electron to fill their outer electron shells. So these elements form ions with a charge of –1.

- Elements in group 6 need 2 electrons to fill their outer shells They form ions with a charge of –2.

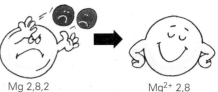

Mg 2,8,2 Mg^{2+} 2,8

Magnesium atoms are only too pleased to get rid of two electrons.

O 2,6 O^{2-} 2,8

Oxygen atoms need two electrons to make them happy.

QUESTIONS

1. What type of elements are on the left of the periodic table?

2. What types of elements have to be reacted to make a covalent substance?

3. Make a table with the headings **Element**, **Group** and **Metal or non-metal**. Look at the periodic table. Fill in your table for the elements Cs, S, Au, Xe, Rb and Pt.

4. What will be the charge on an ion of each of the following elements: magnesium (Mg), aluminium (Al), sulphur (S), calcium (Ca) and rubidium (Rb)?

KEY IDEAS

The periodic table can help us predict what elements are like and how they react.

4.1 *Acids all around us*

Many people think of acids as bubbling, smoking liquids that can 'eat' through solid metal. But lemonade is an acid too.

Sour tasting

The word **acid** means sour. This is true enough for lemons, but it is not a useful way of testing something like sulphuric acid. There are many acidic substances in the world around you.

Some acids are found in fruits. Lemons and oranges contain citric acid. Other foods like tomatoes are rich in vitamin C, which is ascorbic acid. Every cup of tea has a tiny quantity of tannic acid.

It is also common for food that 'goes off' to produce acids. Milk produces an acid and tastes sour if left for several days in a warm place.

So all acids are not the same. Some are 'mild' like lemonade, and others are 'strong' like sulphuric acid.

Fruits contain acids.

Acids in self defence or digestion

Because they are potentially dangerous many acids have to be handled with great care.

This hazard symbol means 'corrosive'.

Nature makes use of the 'dangerous' qualities of acids. You have acid inside you. The digestive juices in your stomach are very acidic. They are used to break down the food you eat to more usable chemicals. The sting in a bee is acidic. Some stinging ants squirt out acid.

This bee sting is acidic.

Making use of acids

Acids are used for flavouring drinks and food because of their sour taste. But acids have a lot more uses:

- from pickling food to making plastics
- from making fibres to producing fertilisers
- from cleaning metals to manufacturing medicines.

Willow bark contains an acid that you would recognise as being like aspirin.

One very useful strong acid is sulphuric acid. About $2\frac{1}{2}$ million tonnes are made in the UK each year. It is used to make a wide range of things.

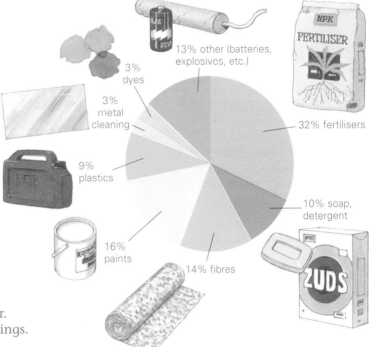

13% other (batteries, explosives, etc.)

3% dyes

3% metal cleaning

32% fertilisers

9% plastics

10% soap, detergent

16% paints

14% fibres

Sulphuric acid is used in UK manufacturing.

Problems with acids

Sulphuric acid reacts very strongly with other substances. It can attack things chemically – it is **corrosive**. Great care is needed when transporting it.

Acid rain comes from the slightly acid nature of the gases made by burning coal. These gases dissolve in rain water and cause problems for lakes, trees and buildings.

Care is needed in transporting acids.

QUESTIONS

1 Complete this sentence:
   Vinegar must be an _____ because it tastes _____ .

2 Write the names of five things mentioned on these pages that contain acids.

3 What are the three main uses of sulphuric acid?

KEY IDEAS

Some acids are mild and are used in food.

Some acids are strong and corrosive. They must be handled with care.

Acids have many important uses.

Acids can occur in nature or be manufactured.

4.2 *How tough are acids and alkalis?*

Some acids are mild enough for us to swallow with our food, but other acids would harm our skin if spilled. What makes the difference?

pH scale

You can measure how cold or hot something is by using a temperature scale. Similarly, you can measure how mild or strong an acid is by using the **pH scale**. This is a range of numbers. The 'p' of pH comes from a German word 'potentz' meaning *power*. So pH measures the power or strength of acids.

The strongest, most dangerous acids are pH 1. Hydrochloric acid is an example. Acids which are not quite so powerful have a higher number. The pH of a bee sting is about 5. By the time you get to pH 7, a substance isn't acid at all. The pH of pure water is 7, which is called **neutral**. So the numbers make a scale of acidity like this:

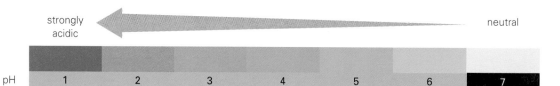

Acids have pH numbers less than 7.

Different strengths

Lemon juice is an acid. It tastes sour, but it doesn't corrode your mouth. It is a weak acid of pH 4. Some low voltage batteries contain acid of about pH 3. This sometimes leaks out and attacks the metal case. Sulphuric acid is pH 1 and is one of the most corrosive acids you ever use. It reacts with many materials including some metals.

Alkalis – the chemical opposites of acids

A bee sting is acidic. But equally painful is the sting in a wasp. This is an **alkali** – the chemical opposite of an acid. Alkalis have different strengths, and the pH scale is used to measure them too.

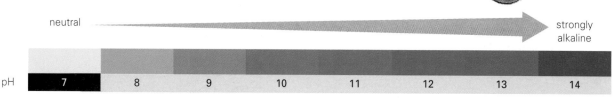

Alkalis have pH numbers greater than 7.

A weak alkali called ammonia is used in many cleaning products for work surfaces. It is pH 8. Sodium hydroxide is pH 14 and is a very strong alkali. It reacts with many materials including fats, turning them into soaps.

Measuring pH

The easiest way to measure pH is to use a substance which 'shows up' or indicates the pH by its colour. Two examples are **universal indicator** and **litmus**. Both these **indicators** can be in a solution or on a strip of paper.

The pH charts on the opposite page show how universal indicator paper changes colour.

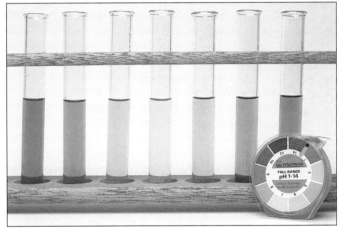

Universal indicator measures a range of pH solutions.

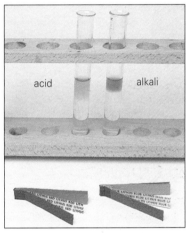

Litmus tells you if a solution is an acid or alkali.

QUESTIONS

1   Draw your own chart from pH 1 to pH 14. Put a label on it for all the items drawn on these pages. For example, lemon juice will go at pH 4.

2   Complete the following sentences:
   a The strongest acid in my chart is _____.
   b The strongest alkali is _____.
   c An example of a weak acid is _____.

3   List these items in order – the strongest acid to the strongest alkali:

   fresh milk (pH = 6.8)   stomach juices (pH = 1.0)
   blood (pH = 7.4)   oven cleaner (pH = 12.5)
   cup of tea (pH = 5.2)   sea water (pH = 7.0)

KEY IDEAS

The pH scale is used to measure the strength of acids and alkalis.

Acids have low numbers, pH 1 to 6.

Alkalis have high numbers, pH 8 to 14.

pH 7 is neutral.

Indicators show the pH of a solution by colour.

4.3 *What can acids do for you?*

How is a battery like a pickled onion, and a fire extinguisher like a cake?

Fire extinguishers and cakes

Acids can produce carbon dioxide gas when they react with chemicals called carbonates. This gas puts out fires. This is the basic idea of how some fire extinguishers work.

To make a light and spongy cake, add a little baking powder to the cake mixture. This contains an acid and a carbonate. These chemicals react when you heat the mixture slowly in the oven. The carbon dioxide gas released makes your cake 'rise'.

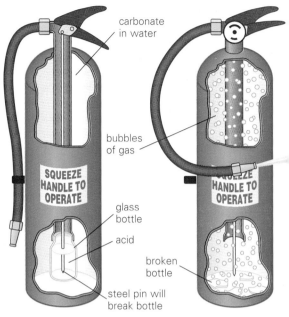

Some fire extinguishers squirt out carbon dioxide gas and water to put out flames.

Perfect cakes from acid and carbonate!

Stopping rusting

Iron and steel **rust** in the air to form iron oxide. Phosphoric acid is used to dissolve this oxide away and leave a clean surface. You can protect against more rusting by coating the clean surface with paint or grease. This keeps the air away from the metal.

Chemicals can help you fight against rust.

Preserving food

Bacteria can make food go 'off'. But they cannot survive in acid conditions, so acids are often used to preserve food. Mild acids which do not affect the flavour are added to juices and jams. Vinegar is used to pickle or preserve food like onions and eggs. Lemon juice stops fruit going brown.

Acids are used to stop some foods going bad.

Making electricity

If you dip two different metals in acid and join them together, a chemical reaction causes electricity to flow between them. This is how a battery works. One metal becomes the positive (+) end of the battery. The other metal becomes the negative (–) end.

In some cases, the chemical reaction can be forced back again with mains electricity. This is how rechargeable batteries work.

The metal inside these batteries reacts with acid to make electricity.

Making new chemicals

Acids react with metals, metal oxides and metal carbonates to produce new chemicals called **salts**. These contain part of the acid joined up with the metal from the other substance. For example, hydro*chloric* acid reacts with *calcium* carbonate to produce *calcium chloride*.

Salts have many important uses.

Now the bad news

While acids can be made to do useful tasks for us, the strong acids with low pH can also cause damage. Acid spilled from a tanker may spread out and try to react with any metals and cement nearby. It would certainly react with any human tissue.

So you must handle acids with care. Acids corrode metals. They slowly 'eat' them away. The metal will get weaker and may eventually break.

QUESTIONS

1 Complete the sentence using these words:

kill   acids   corrosive   damage

_____ react with many materials. They can _____ metals and _____ bacteria. Their hazard label is _____.

2 Pickled food is never sold in metal cans. Why?

3 Limescale is a calcium carbonate which builds up in some kettles. Clare suggests it can be removed with vinegar. When she tries, it works and she see it fizzing. Why?

KEY IDEAS

Acids kill bacteria.

Acids react with metals, metal carbonates and metal oxides. This makes new chemicals called salts.

Acid corrosion can damage materials.

4.4 *Getting rid of the power of acids*

Acids can cause problems from polluted lakes to tooth decay. Even bees sting you with an acid. Can their power be stopped?

If you eat an acid-drop sweet which has a sour taste, and then put some bicarbonate of soda on your tongue, the taste immediately disappears. Chemists describe the destroying of or cancelling out of the power of an acid as **neutralisation**.

Alkalis are most commonly used to neutralise acids because they are at the opposite end of the pH scale.

	acid	+	alkali	→	salt	+	water
	pH below 7		pH above 7		pH 7 (neutral)		pH 7 (neutral)
Colour in universal indicator:	red		blue		green		green

Alkalis destroy the power of acids, and acids destroy the power of alkalis.

Tummy ache

When you eat food, it is digested in your stomach by strong acid in the stomach juices (pH 1). If too much acid is produced, you might get a painful sensation in your stomach – a tummy ache.

One answer is to swallow some medicine containing an alkali to neutralise the extra acid. These medicines are called 'ant-acids'.

Ant-acids remove the power of excess acid, so the tummy ache should go away.

Acid pollution

Coal and oil are burned to supply us with energy, but when they burn they make acidic gases. When it rains, these gases dissolve in the rain water, making the water a dilute acid. This acid rain can damage trees and buildings, and runs into rivers and lakes where it collects. The answer for these polluted lakes and rivers is to add an alkali, like lime, to the water.

Checking the pH of water.

Tooth decay

Your saliva contains all sorts of chemicals and bacteria. Bacteria help start the digestion process off as you chew food. Unfortunately, they can also convert sugar into acids. This acid can rot your teeth. If you eat a biscuit just before you go to sleep, bacteria will produce acid in your saliva all night long! To help stop your teeth rotting, alkali is added to your toothpaste. Regular brushing will help keep the acidity away.

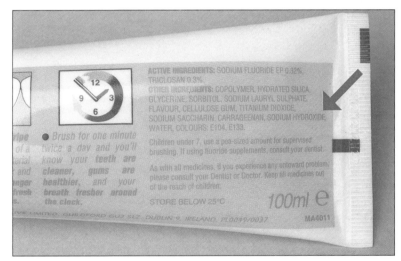

Toothpaste contains alkali to fight tooth decay.

QUESTIONS

1 Copy and complete these sentences:

A pupil spills some hydrochloric acid in the laboratory, so the teacher sprinkles sodium carbonate onto it. The acidic substance was _____ _____ which is neutralised by _____ _____.

2 Acidic insect stings are rubbed with bicarbonate of soda. Nettle stings are alkaline and might be rubbed with vinegar. Why?

3 Farmer Growitt's soil is pH 5. He wishes to grow barley. Barley grows best at pH 8. He adds a certain amount of lime to the soil. Why?

4.5 *Patterns in acids and alkalis*

Acids behave in similar ways, so they must all have something in common. What is it inside acids and alkalis that makes them so reactive?

Look for some clues

When you list the atoms in a substance, you are writing a chemical formula. In this table of acids and their formulas, you might be able to pick out two patterns.

Name of acid	Formula	Non-metals
hydrochloric	HCl	chlorine
sulphuric	H_2SO_4	sulphur and oxygen
phosphoric	H_3PO_4	phosphorus and oxygen
nitric	HNO_3	nitrogen and oxygen

- They all contain the element hydrogen.

- They only contain non-metal elements.

So acids contain hydrogen joined up to a non-metal element.

What makes an acid acidic?

Acids need to be mixed with water before they work as acids. Citric acid is a neutral solid. If water is added to citric acid the pH is about 5. The water releases the hydrogen from the acid as an ion. It is this particle that makes acids acidic.

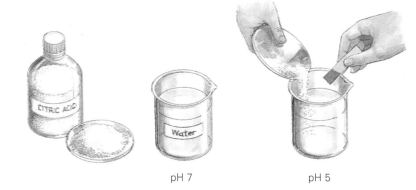

pH 7   pH 5

Acid releases acidic particles into water.

Even pure sulphuric acid behaves strangely without water present. For example, it does not react with metals. However, as soon as water is added it reacts violently.

Acids are made whenever a non-metal is burned in the air and the products are dissolved in water. Sulphur burns to produce sulphur dioxide gas. When this is mixed with water the resulting solution turns indicator red because it is acidic.

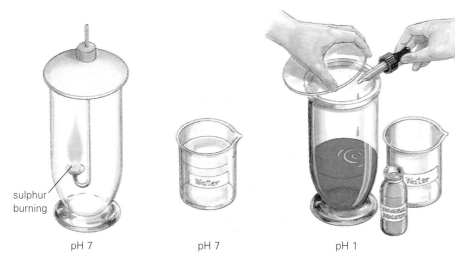

sulphur burning

pH 7   pH 7   pH 1

Non-metal oxides dissolve in water to form acids.

Exhaust fumes from cars contain nitrogen oxide. The heat from car engines has made nitrogen and oxygen in the air join up. On warm, still days this gas builds up in the air. It becomes acidic as it mixes with water vapour in the air. This can irritate the lining of the lungs of people with breathing problems.

Cyclists in cities sometimes wear masks to protect their lungs from acidic fumes and dust.

What makes an alkali alkaline?

Look at this table of alkalis and their formulas for some clues.

- Most alkalis contain a metal element.

- They also contain a hydroxide (OH).

Again, they only work as alkalis when the hydroxide particles dissolve in water to form ions.

Name of alkali	Formula	Metal
sodium hydroxide	NaOH	sodium
potassium hydroxide	KOH	potassium
calcium hydroxide	$Ca(OH)_2$	calcium

And finally

There is a pattern in the periodic table. Metals form alkaline oxides and non-metals form acidic oxides.

Have you noticed something interesting? All acids contain H in their formula, and all alkalis contain OH in their formula. So when acids and alkalis react together they make neutral water, H_2O, as one product.

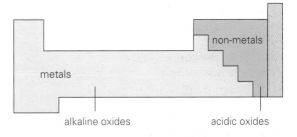

metals

non-metals

alkaline oxides   acidic oxides

QUESTIONS

1 Choose from the pairs to complete these sentences:

When sodium is put into water it fizzes violently and the water turns **alkaline/acidic** with a **low/high** pH, because sodium is a **metal/non-metal** element.

When phosphorus is burned in air it forms a gas which dissolves in water to make a solution with a **low/high** pH. This tells you it is a **metal/non-metal** element.

2 Many fizzy drinks contain carbon dioxide gas dissolved in water. It makes some drinks taste sour. Why?

4.6 Making and naming salts

You are familiar with the salt you sprinkle on chips, but do you know about the other interesting chemicals called salts?

'Table salt' or sodium chloride can be made in the laboratory by reacting hydrochloric acid and sodium hydroxide together. But there are lots of acids and alkalis, so there are lots of different salts.

Naming salts

Salts have two parts to their name. The first part of the name comes from the metal (maybe from a compound), and the 'surname' comes from the acid it reacts with.

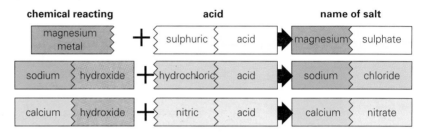

Ways to make salts

To make a salt you need to use the correct acid to match the 'surname' (e.g. hydrochloric acid for a chloride salt). But for the metal part of the salt you have three choices.

- Add the metal itself to the acid – this method can't be used for dangerous metals like sodium, because the reaction happens too quickly. For unreactive metals like copper, the reaction wouldn't happen at all!

acid + metal

add excess of metal to acid

the metal fizzes – it makes hydrogen gas as well as the salt

filter the contents of the beaker to separate unreacted metal

boil off most of the water then leave to evaporate for a few days

heat

Add more than enough metal, to make sure all the acid is used up.

- Add the metal as part of a compound like an alkali – this is a safer method for making salts of reactive metals like sodium.

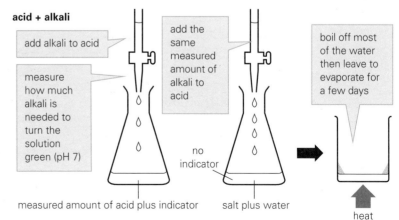

The alkali neutralises the acid when exactly the right amount is added.

68

- Add the metal as the metal carbonate. For example: calcium carbonate added to hydrochloric acid produces calcium chloride, water and carbon dioxide.

acid + metal carbonate

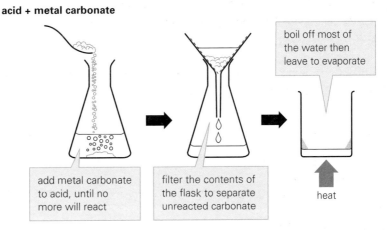

add metal carbonate to acid, until no more will react

filter the contents of the flask to separate unreacted carbonate

boil off most of the water then leave to evaporate

heat

An excess of carbonate will ensure that all the acid is used up.

Getting to the salt

In each case you are left with the salt dissolved in water. It is easy to boil off most of the water, and then leave the solution to evaporate. Over a few days, tiny crystals of the salt appear.

Some salts are made in the laboratory, but others occur naturally in the ground or the sea.

Some useful salts		
Chemical name	**Common name**	**Use**
sodium chloride	table salt	preservative/taste improver
potassium chlorate	saltpetre	explosives
ammonium nitrate	Nitram	fertiliser

Crystalline salts.

QUESTIONS

1 Complete the table:

Acid	Source of metal	Salt produced
nitric	magnesium hydroxide	
	iron	iron sulphate
hydrochloric	calcium carbonate	

2 Draw a labelled diagram for each step in making iron sulphate from iron carbonate and sulphuric acid. Include in your diagram:

a adding metal carbonate to acid

b filtering off any solid

c crystallising.

4.7 Designer metals

Metals are everywhere, from the tiniest battery inside a wrist-watch to the Eiffel Tower. How come they are used in so many ways?

What makes different metals useful			
Object	Metal	Physical property	Chemical property
pipe	copper	flexible	no reaction with water
jewellery	gold	shiny	no reaction with air or water
battery	zinc	strong	reacts with acid to make electricity

You can see from the table that different metals have different uses. A metal good for one job may not be any good for another job. The main reason why a metal is chosen for a particular job is because of its special properties.

The Eiffel Tower in Paris was built of solid iron in 1889.

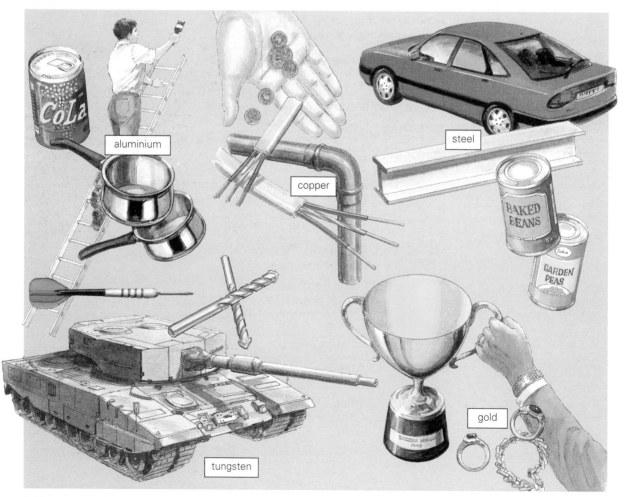

aluminium

copper

steel

gold

tungsten

Different metals have different uses.

Two sorts of properties

The **physical properties** of a metal include its strength, how well it conducts electricity, and how easily it melts. For example, mercury is an unusual metal because it melts at −39°C and so it is a liquid at room temperature.

Metals also have **chemical properties**. Metals are chemicals and they may react with other substances. These reactions may affect their physical properties. For example, a rusty car body panel will be weaker than a new panel, and so will not protect a driver so well in a crash.

Many metals react with the chemicals around them, like air or water. This reaction is called **corrosion**. It would be no use making a wedding ring out of iron, because it would slowly corrode, and turn dirty brown and powdery.

Mercury is a liquid metal used in thermometers.

We need to understand how metals react with other chemicals. Some metals react with acids. It would be no good transporting sulphuric acid in steel containers, because the acid would corrode away the metal and leak out. Some metals like zinc react with the acids in food, so these metals are not used for food cans.

If a bicycle is not protected, the metal will soon rust away.

QUESTIONS

1 Why is steel used to make cranes?

2 Give two advantages of using gold to make trophies instead of wood.

3 Choose from the pairs to complete the sentences:

   a Aluminium ladders are replacing wooden ones because they are **lighter/heavier**.

   b Aluminium ladders **do/do not** rot or corrode.

   c Aluminium ladders can hold **more/less** weight before being damaged.

4.8 *The premier metal league*

The behaviour of metals is a bit like a football league table, but the results of each game are always the same!

If you take nine common metals and do a whole series of different experiments with them (like heat them in air, add water, add acid) you will soon spot a pattern. The metal that is dangerously violent in your first experiment will always be the most reactive in all of the other experiments. Likewise, the slowest-reacting metal will always be slow and unreactive.

This is called the **reactivity series.** It is like a batting order. During a cricket season you might list the best batsman to the worst. In Wimbledon fortnight, tennis players are ranked from the number one player. There is one important difference in sport – the ranking changes each season. Manchester United do not always win the championship. But in chemistry, the top metal is always the most reactive, and the order never changes.

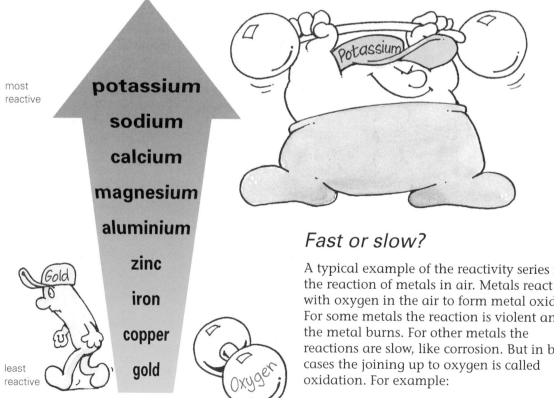

League tables help make predictions.

most reactive

potassium

sodium

calcium

magnesium

aluminium

zinc

iron

copper

gold

least reactive

The reactivity series.

Fast or slow?

A typical example of the reactivity series is the reaction of metals in air. Metals react with oxygen in the air to form metal oxides. For some metals the reaction is violent and the metal burns. For other metals the reactions are slow, like corrosion. But in both cases the joining up to oxygen is called oxidation. For example:

magnesium + oxygen → magnesium oxide

Magnesium (high up the reactivity series) burns in air with a very bright flame. It was used in flares, and is still a component of fireworks.

Iron is lower in the series and does not burn so spectacularly, unless it is powdered. It will rust slowly.

Iron corrodes slowly.

Gold (right at the bottom of the series) does not burn or corrode in air, which is partly why it is used in jewellery.

This ancient gold mask has not corroded.

Sparklers are made with reactive metals.

QUESTIONS

1 Look at the reactivity series and complete the sentences:

  a _____ is the most reactive metal.

  b _____ is the least reactive metal.

  c _____ and _____ are more reactive than magnesium.

  d _____ and _____ are less reactive than iron.

2 Gold earrings do not go rusty. What does this tell you about gold's place in the reactivity series?

3 Calcium is sometimes used in fireworks. It burns well in the air to make a red flame. Write the word equation for this reaction.

KEY IDEAS

The way metals react with other chemicals can be predicted from the reactivity series.

Metals at the top are more reactive.

Metals at the bottom are less reactive.

Metals react with the oxygen from the air to form metal oxides.

4.9 *Predicting how metals behave*

Some metals do not react with water, some react with steam, and some react violently with cold water. Is it possible to predict how a metal will react?

Reacting with water

Metals that react with water give off hydrogen gas and make the water alkaline.

  metal + water → metal hydroxide + hydrogen

e.g. potassium + water → potassium hydroxide + hydrogen
           (an alkali)

The metal at the top of the reactivity series, potassium, is very violent in its reaction with water. It catches fire on contact with water, often exploding. Copper, near the bottom of the series, does not react with water, which is why it is used for water pipes.

Reactive metals have to be used with great care.

Reacting with acids

Metals react more vigorously with acids than with water. They make a salt and hydrogen gas.

  metal + acid   → salt   + hydrogen

e.g. zinc + hydrochloric acid → zinc chloride + hydrogen

Magnesium fizzes very rapidly, because it is high up in the reactivity series. Iron bubbles slowly. Gold or copper do not react at all, because they are at the bottom of the series.

Sulphuric acid is not transported in tankers made of just steel (which is mainly iron). Instead, the steel is lined with glass, plastic or lead. Cavities in teeth could not be filled with iron, because acidic food and drinks would make the hole reappear! Gold fillings might be a better choice, because gold is unreactive.

To make hydrogen gas, you use zinc and an acid. A metal higher up in the series reacts too violently. Metals lower down in the series will not work.

An unreactive metal is used for teeth as well as jewellery!

The most reactive win!

Many chemical reactions are competitions. The most reactive metal wins. If you mix copper oxide and magnesium powder, you set up a competition between copper and magnesium for the oxide. You can probably predict who will win!

magnesium + copper oxide → magnesium oxide + copper

These reactions are useful. They are called **displacement reactions**. Aluminium can displace the iron in iron oxide to make iron and aluminium oxide. The aluminium grabs the oxygen from the iron so violently that the iron turns white hot and melts. This reaction was used to mend broken railway tracks.

aluminium + iron oxide → iron + aluminium oxide

You can also coat a metal with another metal. If you dip an iron knife in a solution of copper sulphate, the iron pushes copper off the sulphate and the copper is deposited onto the knife.

Reactive metals are like chemical bullies!

QUESTIONS

1   Complete the sentences:

Copper is an unreactive metal because it is near the _____ of the reactivity series.

Potassium has to be stored in oil because it is at the _____ of the series.

2   Make up your own cartoon drawing to show magnesium taking oxygen from copper.

3   Tin is used inside a can of apples to stop the acid juice attacking the steel.

   a Where is tin in the reactivity series, low or high?

   b How do you know this?

4.10 *Cures for corrosion*

A rust mark on a car doesn't just spoil its appearance. Why is corrosion a problem? How can you stop it?

What causes the problem?

If you leave some metals outside in damp weather they begin to corrode, as the surface of the metal begins to break up. Gases in the air, together with water can make some metals corrode. You can demonstrate this in the laboratory.

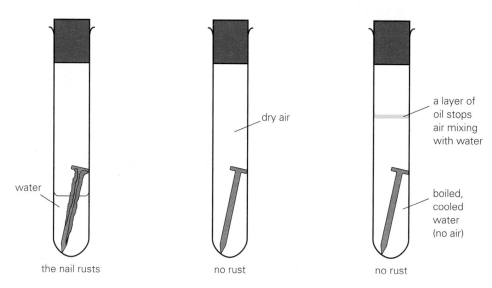

water

the nail rusts

dry air

no rust

a layer of oil stops air mixing with water

boiled, cooled water (no air)

no rust

Both water and air are needed for iron to rust.

Look in the table at the results of leaving metals for a period of time. Some would be useless after an hour, others after a day.

The reactivity series again!

The more reactive metals corrode easily and so they are not very useful. Sodium is difficult to store and is kept in a sealed bottle under a layer of oil. This keeps air and water away.

Many of the metals like gold and silver at the bottom of the series do not corrode but unfortunately they are also rare and therefore expensive!

Metal	Corrosion after 1 hour	Corrosion after 1 day
sodium	dull tarnish	all white ash
magnesium	slight white coat	thick white coat
iron	slight	brown rust on surface
copper	none	slight
gold	none	none

Keeping metals useful

Fortunately the corrosion of the useful metals like iron can be stopped, or at least slowed down. Here are some ways of protecting against rust:

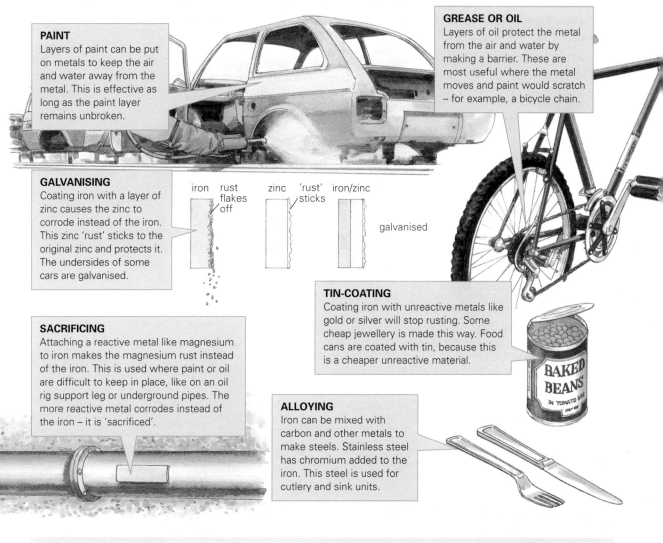

PAINT
Layers of paint can be put on metals to keep the air and water away from the metal. This is effective as long as the paint layer remains unbroken.

GREASE OR OIL
Layers of oil protect the metal from the air and water by making a barrier. These are most useful where the metal moves and paint would scratch – for example, a bicycle chain.

GALVANISING
Coating iron with a layer of zinc causes the zinc to corrode instead of the iron. This zinc 'rust' sticks to the original zinc and protects it. The undersides of some cars are galvanised.

iron   rust flakes off   zinc   'rust' sticks   iron/zinc

galvanised

TIN-COATING
Coating iron with unreactive metals like gold or silver will stop rusting. Some cheap jewellery is made this way. Food cans are coated with tin, because this is a cheaper unreactive material.

SACRIFICING
Attaching a reactive metal like magnesium to iron makes the magnesium rust instead of the iron. This is used where paint or oil are difficult to keep in place, like on an oil rig support leg or underground pipes. The more reactive metal corrodes instead of the iron – it is 'sacrificed'.

ALLOYING
Iron can be mixed with carbon and other metals to make steels. Stainless steel has chromium added to the iron. This steel is used for cutlery and sink units.

QUESTIONS

1   Complete the sentence:
    Corrosion is when a metal reacts with _____ and _____.

2   Write a few sentences and draw diagrams to show how you would investigate the success of two methods to stop nails rusting.

3   List three possible practical methods to stop a car roof-rack from rusting.

KEY IDEAS

Water and air are the main causes of corrosion.

Reactive metals corrode most easily.

Unreactive metals hardly corrode at all.

Rusting of iron can be prevented in several ways.

5.1 *The air we breathe*

Where is all the air pollution we read about?
You can't see it, so is it a lot of fuss about nothing?

Hidden gases

Gases are difficult to see and feel. Most of them are colourless and spread out so we forget they are around us. A few gases can be detected by your nose because they have smells. Common everyday smells include perfumes, fried bacon and bad eggs.

You can tell this flower is a rose just by smelling it.

A lot of nothing?

Smells soon fade as they are diluted by other gases in the air around us. If you put a drop of ink in a glass of water, the water goes blue. Put it in a swimming pool and it will disappear. It is the same with smells. When you barbecue sausages there is an obvious smell, which disappears as the smell spreads or *diffuses* into the rest of the air.

How fresh is the air?

A healthy person breathes in about 15 000 litres of air every day. This air is in contact with an area inside the lungs the size of a tennis court! Oxygen from the air passes from the lungs into the bloodstream.

The balance of gases in air must be correct for people to breathe easily. Too much of a certain gas in the air may affect you. For example, smoke in a room makes some people cough.

When you can breathe well your body stays fit.

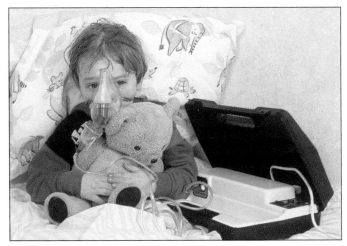

Some people need help with breathing.

A never-changing mixture?

There are different amounts of all of the gases on Earth. The balance has remained roughly the same for 200 million years. Recently, scientists have shown how certain gases released into the air are causing major problems. These gases are called **pollutants**. Their damaging effects often take a long time to appear.

Air pollution			
Problem	**Cause**	**Damage**	**Solution**
acid rain	power stations burn fossil fuels like oil and coal, releasing acidic gases; hot car engines cause gases in the air to react and make acidic fumes	may alter the natural pH of rivers and land, and damage trees and buildings	clean up exhaust gases and burn less fossil fuel
ozone hole	**chlorofluorocarbons** (CFCs) are used in some aerosols, for making refrigerators cold and as solvents; they react with ozone gas in the upper atmosphere	the **ozone layer** protects us from the sun's dangerous rays – if there is a hole in it, the rays get through, causing skin cancers and eye problems	replace the CFCs with other, less harmful chemicals
hydrocarbons	unburned fuel from vehicles and filling stations evaporates into the air	possible cause of some cancers	cut down evaporation of fuels, and clean up car exhaust fumes
carbon monoxide	fuels burn in air to form carbon dioxide – poor air supply when burning fuels produces carbon monoxide instead	very poisonous, causing tiredness, headaches and sometimes death	maintain equipment such as gas fires properly
lead particles	cars using leaded petrol	possible damage to the nervous system, especially in young children	car engines which use unleaded fuels

QUESTIONS

1   The words with black letters are scrambled. Rearrange the letters to make words:

   lenca air is vital for life. **olplteud** air contains **sseag** which harm the Earth and living things.

2   Draw a poster for one of the pollution problems in the table. Suggest how to solve the problem.

3   Limestone is an alkali. It is sometimes put in factory chimneys. How might this deal with acid fumes?

5.2 *What is in clean air?*

You can't see the gases in the air. So what are they like, and what use are they?

Air – a mixture of gases

Most of the air is a gas called nitrogen, but there are many others.

Nitrogen

Nitrogen is an unreactive gas. A healthy body copes best with oxygen diluted in nitrogen, for breathing. But deep-sea divers have to dilute their oxygen with helium, because nitrogen would dissolve in their blood when diving.

Most nitrogen is used to make ammonia (NH_3) for fertilisers.

At low temperatures (below $-180°C$) nitrogen becomes a liquid. Liquid nitrogen acts like a deep freezer. It can freeze blood and sperm, keeping them fresh for many years.

Because it is so unreactive, nitrogen is useful for stopping some foods going off. It is used instead of air to fill crisp packets, to stop the crisps reacting with oxygen.

Oxygen

Oxygen makes up about 21% of the air. It is produced by green plants. It is a reactive gas which joins up with most elements.

Most living things need oxygen to keep their bodies working. When substances burn they join up with oxygen. Without oxygen there would be no coal burning to make electricity, no motor vehicles, Bunsen burners or gas boilers. There would be no rusting of iron, paint would never dry, there would be nothing for you to breathe.

In the UK about 2 million tonnes of oxygen are removed from the air industrially each year. Most is used to make steel. Oxygen is used in hospitals, to help breathing in very weak patients. It is mixed with fuels to make rockets and explosives.

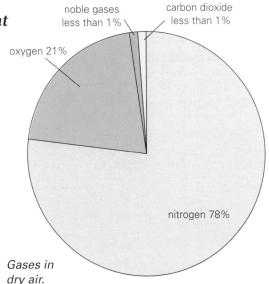

noble gases less than 1%

carbon dioxide less than 1%

oxygen 21%

nitrogen 78%

Gases in dry air.

Nitrogen is a liquid at very low temperatures.

Extra oxygen helps substances burn quickly.

Carbon dioxide

A very small proportion of the air is made up of carbon dioxide. This is a fairly unreactive, but important gas.

Most living things breathe out carbon dioxide as a waste gas. Fossil fuels produce it when they burn. Plants and trees take it in and use it to make new chemicals.

Carbon dioxide makes the fizz in drinks and the foam in fire-extinguishers. Dry ice effects come from solid carbon dioxide. It is also used to make decaffeinated coffee.

Solid carbon dioxide is used as dry ice on stage.

Noble gases

These unreactive gases like argon are used where air might allow a substance to burn, for example in light bulbs. This family of inert or unreactive gases can be separated from air. Noble gases have many uses – from argon in lightbulbs to helium in airships.

Water

Water is present in small amounts in the air as rain or moisture. The exact amount of water depends on the temperature and the place. It partly determines the weather.

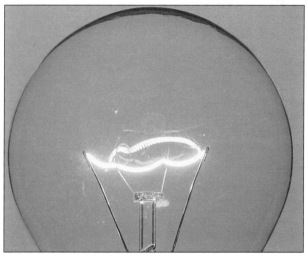

If this light bulb was filled with air instead of argon, its filament would burn away.

QUESTIONS

1 Complete the following sentences:
   a Most of the air is the gas _____ .
   b _____ is the gas you need to breathe in.
   c _____ is the gas you breathe out.

2 Draw a table with the headings **Gas** and **Percentage in air**.
   a Look at the pie chart, then fill in your table.
   b Draw a picture to show one use of each of the gases.

3 Match the gas in air with the process:
   oxygen   making fertilisers
   nitrogen   making fizzy drinks
   argon   filling light bulbs
   carbon dioxide   making fuels burn

KEY IDEAS

Air is a mixture of gases.

Most of the air is nitrogen.

Gases in air are used in many different ways.

5.3 The Earth sits in a greenhouse

The Earth is warming up. Is this good news or bad?

The problem of global warming is due to the production of certain gases. Some gases are formed by natural processes. Others are made by man-made reactions. Carbon dioxide gets into the air both naturally (by breathing) and from human activity (when a fuel burns).

The greenhouse in the garden

Gardeners use a greenhouse to help grow plants. Light from the Sun passes through the glass into the greenhouse. When the light hits the soil or plants, it changes to heat energy and warms them. The heat made this way cannot get back through the glass very easily, and so is trapped. The air in the greenhouse becomes warmer than the air outside. In the summer it may get *too* hot.

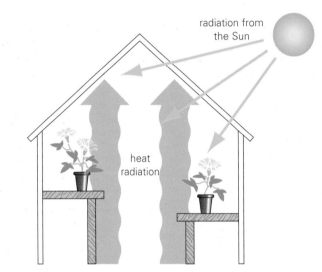

The garden greenhouse traps heat from the Sun.

A global greenhouse

The Earth is surrounded by the gases of the air. These gases act like the glass of the greenhouse. They let the Sun's rays through, but only slowly let the heat back out into space. They behave like a duvet. This keeps the average temperature of the Earth just right to allow us to survive. Without this effect, the Earth would be far too hot in the day and freezing cold at night. As the amount of these gases builds up in the air, the duvet gets thicker and the Earth gets warmer.

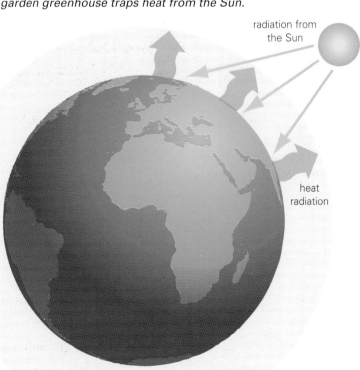

The global greenhouse also traps heat from the Sun.

Nice hot summers

A warmer Earth doesn't mean simply hotter summers in Britain! The effect is complicated, because the temperatures change so much from day to day and place to place. It is difficult to measure slight changes in temperature over the years. Most scientists believe there is a build up of greenhouse gases, and they agree that between 1970 and 1990 the average temperature of the Earth rose by 0.4°C.

There may be consequences of further temperature rises. It could cause a lot of ice to melt, which would make the sea level rise, causing widespread flooding. It could also affect the weather, and the sorts of plants and crops that grow.

More bananas, but less bread?

The wind and the sun are two energy sources we can use to make electricity.

What can be done?

To slow down this greenhouse effect we need to cut down on any gases causing the 'duvet' to thicken. The most important gas is carbon dioxide, produced by burning fuel. If we burned less fossil fuel, we could reduce the amount of carbon dioxide in the air.

But we all consume more and more electricity, and people do not want to give up motor cars. Industry requires vast amounts of energy. Any changes may hit developing countries especially badly. Future scientists might discover new energy sources, or change engine design.

Electric cars make less carbon dioxide pollution.

QUESTIONS

1 Complete the sentences:
   The Earth and its gases are like a _____ . Gases around us are like a giant _____.
   More of these gases may cause the Earth to _____ up.

2 Design a poster to describe one cause of global warming, and one solution.

3 Why do you think alternative energy sources may help solve the problems of global warming?

5.4 *Living things recycle carbon*

*Carbon is the element of life.
Scientists searching for life on other
planets look for carbon. Why?*

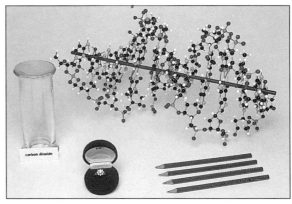
Carbon is found in all these things ...

Carbon

Diamond and the graphite in pencil lead are
made from pure carbon. Carbon is found in
millions of compounds inside living things, and
in things that were once living. It forms
molecules from simple ones like carbon dioxide,
to complex ones like the DNA in your genes.

Carbon inside you

Most of your body is made of carbon compounds. It is present in
blood, muscles and even your breath. Your carbon source is
the food you eat. Potato, sugar, bread, rice and pasta are all
rich in **carbohydrates** (chemicals made of carbon,
hydrogen and oxygen). All animals get their carbon
from the plants or meat they eat.

More and more carbon

Carbon builds up in the soil and the air in several ways.

- Animals get rid of some carbon as carbon dioxide when
  they breathe out. This is part of the chemical process
  called **respiration**.

- Some carbon is lost from animals as they **excrete** waste
  from their bodies.

- Carbon goes into the ground when living things die.

- The remains of dead things and excrement will be rotted
  down by bacteria, which give out carbon dioxide.

Each step adds to the amount of carbon dioxide in the atmosphere.

Using it up again

... and in carbohydrates too.

All this carbon doesn't go to waste. It is recycled. Plants use up the carbon
dioxide by turning it back into compounds like carbohydrates, in a process
called **photosynthesis**. These compounds are eaten by animals, and the
cycle continues.

An atom of carbon might start as carbon dioxide in the air, be used up by a
dandelion, eaten by a sheep, eaten by a human then breathed out again.

A large amount of carbon dioxide also dissolves in the oceans.

Fossil fuels

Not all plants and small sea creatures are eaten. Millions of years ago some were buried under the ground or sea. Pressure and heat turned the fossil remains into fuels. Plants became coal, and sea creatures became oil. These have been mined and burned for energy, releasing more carbon dioxide.

The carbon cycle

The amount of carbon dioxide in the air has remained roughly the same for thousands of years. It may be a small percentage of air (0.035%) but it is still 2750 million million tonnes!

If more of the world's forests are chopped down, there will be less carbon dioxide removed from the air by trees. If we continue to burn more and more fuel, there will be more carbon dioxide in the air. These two effects both add seriously to the greenhouse effect and possibly global warming.

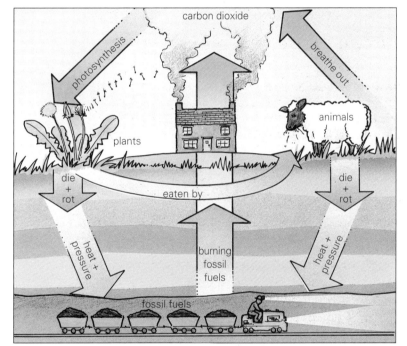

QUESTIONS

1 Choose from the pairs to complete the sentences:

a Carbon is **put into/taken out of** the air by respiration, and **put into/taken out of** the air by burning.

b Carbon is **put into/taken out of** the air by growing plants during photosynthesis.

2 Why are we all encouraged to plant more trees?

3 Write a few sentences about the life of a carbon atom – from a piece of coal being burned, to being part of a plant, an animal, and then back into the air.

KEY IDEAS

All living things contain carbon.

All living things create a global recycling system for carbon.

Human activity is almost certainly upsetting the balance.

5.5 Naturally clean

When you turn on a tap, where does the water come from? When you pull out the plug, where does the waste water go?

A pipe supplying London's water.

Where does water come from?

A tap.

Where does the tap get it from?

A pipe, of course!

Yes, but where does the pipe get it from?

A bigger pipe, silly!

The big pipes are supplied from a water treatment works. Here the water is cleaned, using sand to filter out the finer solid dirt. Then chemicals are added, like chlorine, to kill the germs.

Water is treated to make it clean.

Yes, but where does the treatment works get water?

From reservoirs and lakes.

Rivers and streams provide water for the lakes. They get water from the rain or snow, which come from the sky.

But how does rain form?

Lakes and reservoirs store water for treatment.

The water cycle

As water in the oceans warms up, some of it evaporates. It turns to a gas called water vapour. High in the sky, this water vapour forms clouds which get blown around by the winds.

When the clouds are pushed to somewhere cooler, the water vapour condenses back into a liquid. It falls as rain.

In the lab, you can make water vapour by heating water over a Bunsen burner. The sea must be heated by the sun.

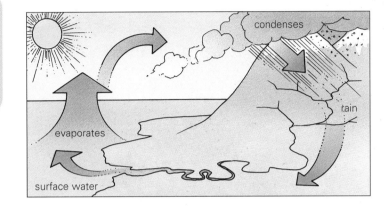

evaporates

condenses

rain

surface water

Where does waste water go?

It goes down the sink or toilet into a sewage pipe, which joins up to a bigger sewage pipe.

The pipe takes it to a sewage works first. Here the big rubbish is filtered out – like rags, and branches from trees. Most solid sludge is filtered out too. Bacteria are used to digest all of this waste. The bacteria produce a fertiliser, and give off a gas which can be burned. This helps to power the sewage works.

After further careful filtering, the more or less clean water is put back into the river.

So water is recycled around – from seas, to clouds, to rain, to rivers and lakes. We tap into the water supply, dirty the water, clean it, and return it.

Could the water I drink have been drunk before?

Yes, because of this water cycle. Water is a solvent and substances dissolve in it. But most of the harmful ones are removed before the water returns to your home.

QUESTIONS

1. Complete these sentences:

   Water _____ from the sea by the _____ of the sun. It rises to make _____. Rain falls, filling _____ which flow back into the _____.

2. Write a story called 'The life of a water molecule'. Describe how the water molecule gets from the sea into your cup of tea, and back to the sea again.

3. Draw diagrams as a flow chart to explain the water cycle. Label each diagram.

KEY IDEAS

Water is recycled by natural processes.

Treatment works clean our water for drinking.

Sewage works clean our waste water before returning it to rivers.

5.6 Food from the air

Ask scientists what is the most important chemical reaction known, and they will probably all say the same thing. Photosynthesis!

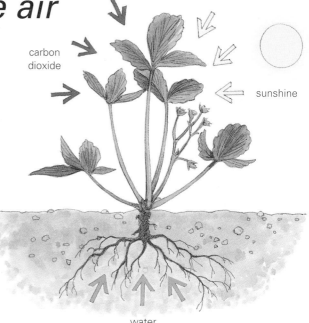

carbon dioxide

sunshine

Plants take in the ingredients they need to make food by photosynthesis.

water

Smartiplants

Plants make their own food. They take light energy from the Sun and change it into chemical energy, which they use to make new plant material. This process is called photosynthesis.

The chemicals they need to start with are mostly water and carbon dioxide.

The chemicals that the plants make are carbohydrates and oxygen.

A green machine

A special green chemical material called **chlorophyll** is found in the leaves of plants. This does all the clever chemistry in photosynthesis. It is a very fast chemical reaction, occurring about a billion times every second in each molecule. A plant has many millions of molecules of chlorophyll. The carbohydrates they produce make the plant grow.

The process is called *photosynthesis* because *photo* means to do with light, and *synthesis* means to make something (like a synthesiser makes music).

carbon dioxide + water + light $\longrightarrow$ carbohydrate + oxygen

raw materials $\longrightarrow$ products

Very good news

Photosynthesis is wonderful news because it:

- traps the sun's energy effectively

- produces food for the world

- makes oxygen for us to breathe

- removes carbon dioxide from the air.

Photosynthesis produces food to feed us.

Successful photosynthesis

The ideal conditions for plants to grow are when there is:

- enough light

- enough carbon dioxide

- enough water

- the correct temperature

As the temperature drops, the speed of photosynthesis slows down. If it gets too cold it stops altogether. The 'green machine' has to shut down when there is no energy to run it. After a while, plants lose their green colour and some shed their leaves. This saves energy for the winter.

Early plants

Many millions of years ago, the Earth's atmosphere was quite different from ours today. It contained mainly carbon dioxide, some ammonia and water vapour. These gases came from all the volcanic activity on Earth at that time.

When the first green plants appeared there was little oxygen, so they 'polluted' the existing atmosphere with the oxygen produced by photosynthesis. A primitive air containing oxygen formed. The level of oxygen steadily increased. Oxygen-breathing creatures began to appear – and from them came animals like us!

Without the correct balance of temperature and water, photosynthesis slows down and little food is produced.

Primitive plants and animals lived in a world without oxygen in the air.

Copying the green machine

Plants capture energy for us. Can scientists design a molecule like chlorophyll to do just that in a test tube – to convert sunshine into chemical energy? This could be used to make electricity! There has been no success as yet. This is a challenge facing scientists for many years to come.

QUESTIONS

1   Complete the sentences:

   a Green plants produce _____ and _____.

   b Plants need _____ and _____ and _____ to grow properly.

2   Some gardeners heat their greenhouses at night with a paraffin burner, which gives out heat and carbon dioxide. Why?

3   Write, in your own words, why photosynthesis is so important.

KEY IDEAS

Plants grow by photosynthesis.

Plants need water, carbon dioxide and sunlight to grow.

Plants make carbohydrates and oxygen.

Photosynthesis is vital for all life.

5.7 *Getting nitrogen to work for us*

You get the nitrogen your body needs from the food you eat. This comes from plants, and animals that eat plants. But where do plants get nitrogen from?

Why nitrogen?

Nitrogen is needed to make certain molecules inside plants, especially for seed production. Nitrogen is in the air, but plants cannot use it. This is because it goes around as N_2 molecules, and the two atoms making it up are tightly joined. Compounds of nitrogen, like nitrates, are easier for plants to use.

Turning the nitrogen from the air into compounds that plants can use is called **nitrogen fixing**. There are four main ways of fixing nitrogen.

■ Lightning

The energy of a giant spark of lightning can break up nitrogen molecules, forcing the atoms to combine with oxygen in the air. This forms nitrogen oxide gas, which dissolves in rain water to make nitrogen compounds. These soak into the ground, for plants to absorb through their roots.

Nitrogen molecules need immense energy to split.

■ Natural fertilisers

Plants and animals are made with proteins, which contain nitrogen. Decaying plants and animal waste are rotted down by bacteria, which produce natural nitrogen **fertiliser** in the soil. Plants use these nitrogen compounds to grow properly.

Unfortunately, other bacteria can actually break up these nitrogen compounds, and turn them back into useless nitrogen gas!

Decaying plants provide useful food for growing plants.

Artificial fertilisers

A chemical factory can convert nitrogen in the air (N_2) to compounds containing ammonia (NH_3). These compounds are added by farmers to the land as fertilisers. These provide nitrogen for the plants to grow. Without fertilisers, the world would be short of food.

Nitrogen-making plants

A few plants contain special bacteria in their roots. These bacteria can split nitrogen in the air. Beans, clover and peas are examples. Gardeners can grow these plants on quite poor soil without fertilisers. These plants are useful because they put nitrogen back into the soil, if they are dug back into the ground afterwards.

The nitrogen cycle

These four processes recycle nitrogen.

For example:

- A nitrogen molecule in the air might be split by lightning, washed into the soil, and taken into a plant through its roots to help it grow.

- Sheep eat the plant and use the protein to make wool. You buy the wool in socks.

- Later, when the socks rot at the local dump, nitrogen compounds are returned to the soil, where bacteria turn it back into nitrogen.

- This gas is released into the air, for the cycle to start again.

Chemicals can add nitrogen to the soil.

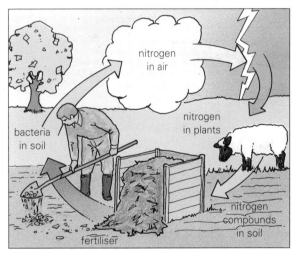

Nitrogen-fixing bacteria help these plants grow.

QUESTIONS

1 Rearrange the letters to complete the sentences.

Nitrogen is present in the **ria** but has to be changed into **gnoeirtn scumdpoon** to be used by plants. **glinthing** and **cabritea** are two ways nature fixes nitrogen.

2 Write a letter to Farmer Growitt to explain four sources of nitrogen for his barley.

3 Produce a cartoon story called 'The life of a nitrogen atom'. Include at least three stages.

5.8 *Ammonia and the Haber process*

We know that ammonia is an important source of nitrogen for plants. But did you know that ammonia got its name from camel dung?

I hope they invent central heating soon!

In ancient Egypt, there were temples to the god, Amun. Being mostly desert, there was no source of heat for the cold nights. So the Egyptians piled up camel dung under the temple floor, which heated up as the dung rotted down. It also smelled, and the pong was called 'Amunia'. So goes one story of how ammonia got its name!

What's it like?

Ammonia is the only alkaline gas (it has a high pH). It is very soluble in water. It is lighter than air, and it smells. The smell is well known, because ammonia is given off from rotting fish, smelling salts and stale urine in babies' nappies. It contains nitrogen and hydrogen. Its formula is NH_3.

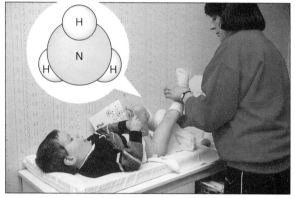

Ammonia has a familiar smell!

Why is it important ?

Plants need a good supply of the element nitrogen to grow into healthy crops. If there is not enough nitrogen available in the ground, fertiliser is needed. Ammonia is the key ingredient in nitrogen fertilisers.

With nitrogen fertiliser ...   *and without.*

Fritz Haber.

From explosives to food supply

During the First World War, the Germans could not get nitrates for explosives because of a naval blockade. Fritz Haber and Karl Bosch were two German chemists who knew a lot about the chemistry of nitrogen. They tried manufacturing ammonia, for conversion to explosives and as fertilisers.

Making ammonia is a difficult reaction to do, because the molecules can change back again into nitrogen and hydrogen. This is called a **reversible reaction**. Notice the double arrow in the equation.

nitrogen + hydrogen $\rightleftharpoons$ ammonia

Haber worked out the special conditions needed to force the reaction in one direction – to make more ammonia. These included a catalyst of iron, a high pressure of 200 atmospheres, and a temperature of 400°C. This made some ammonia. The gases that did not react were recycled through the factory again and again until they did make ammonia.

The nitrogen for this process comes from the air. The hydrogen is made by reacting natural gas (methane) and water.

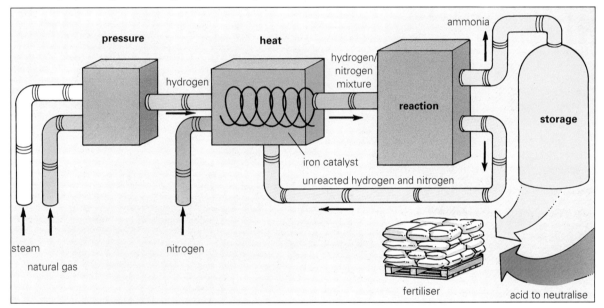

Ammonia can be manufactured by the Haber process.

QUESTIONS

1 Choose some of these words to complete the sentence:
   **nitrogen oxygen hydrogen catalyst
   ammonia Haber reversible**

   _____ and _____ are made into
   _____ by the _____ process.

2 Haber's process is one of the most important ever invented. Why is such a smelly chemical like ammonia vital for the world?

3 Design an experiment to show the effect of a fertiliser. You are given a packet of grass seed, cotton wool, water, a tray, and a solution of fertiliser.

   Explain how you would set up the experiment, and how you would get some results.

5.9 *Feeding the world*

Why can't you just sow a few seeds, and leave it to nature to produce enough food for the world?

Plants need water, carbon dioxide and sunlight before they will grow. They also need small amounts of special nutrients to grow strong and healthy. There are three main nutrient elements – nitrogen, phosphorus and potassium. These help plants to fight off disease, and to produce better flowers and a better crop.

Rice grows well in this fertile area.

In the olden days

In past times, farmers and gardeners would leave an area of land with no crops for a season, so that it could naturally recover the nitrogen needed by the next crop. They then realised that nitrogen could be added to the ground using farmyard manure or compost. Today, the nitrogen is added in a more concentrated way with artificial fertilisers.

Why not use nitrogen gas?

Unfortunately, most plants cannot fix nitrogen gas from the air. But chemists can help to solve this problem by breaking up the nitrogen molecules. They make new compounds where the nitrogen atoms are not so strongly joined.

Fertilisers increase the amount of food produced.

Why not ammonia?

Ammonia is a compound of nitrogen, but it is difficult to use itself as a fertiliser because:

- it is a gas and would blow away
- it is very soluble in water and would wash away
- it is alkaline when dissolved in water and would increase the pH of the soil, making it unsuitable for most plants.

Many plants need an acidic soil.

So ammonia is turned into a neutral salt using an acid.

If you add an acid to ammonia, you get an ammonium salt. These are crystals, with a neutral pH. The main salts made are:

nitric + ammonia → ammonium
 acid   nitrate

sulphuric + ammonia → ammonium
 acid   sulphate

hydrochloric + ammonia → ammonium
 acid   chloride

These are all fertilisers, containing nitrogen in a form plants can take up easily. They are white crystalline materials, easily put on gardens or fields.

0.75% nitrogen

1.5% nitrogen

15% nitrogen

Artificial fertilisers contain more nitrogen.

A perfect solution?

These salts are quite soluble in water. So when it rains, they may dissolve and wash out of the ground. They then find their way into rivers and lakes. The extra nitrogen can make the plants and algae in the rivers grow rapidly.

The difficulty comes when these plants rot. Bacteria rotting them use up the oxygen in the river. The fish and other river animals can't get enough oxygen, and so they die. This problem is called **eutrophication**. The word actually means 'over-eating'. It causes stagnant water where nothing can live.

Fertilisers are a source of water pollution.

QUESTIONS

1. Give two reasons why ammonium chloride is a good fertiliser but ammonia is *not*.
2. Make a list of the chemicals a plant needs to grow well.
3. Explain to Farmer Growitt why he should not put fertiliser down if the weather forecast predicts rain.

6.1 *Is rock useful?*

The Earth provides the raw materials for us to use.
From rocks we get metals, glass and concrete.
From crude oil we get fuels and plastics.

Scissors

If you wanted to buy some scissors, you would go to a shop. The shop gets them from a supplier, who gets them from the manufacturer. Manufacturers produce the handles, blades and rivets using steel from the steel mill. But where does the raw material for steel come from?

Earth, air and water?

All the things surrounding you are made from different substances. But the substances have to come from raw material from somewhere on our planet:

- ■ *The air* provides gases like oxygen used in hospitals, and nitrogen in fertilisers.

- ■ *The oceans* provide chemicals like table salt, used to preserve food. Compounds from the sea can be broken into elements and used. For example, the element bromine is extracted from salts in the Dead Sea using electricity. Bromine is used in photography.

- ■ *The Earth* provides many materials from the rocks beneath you.

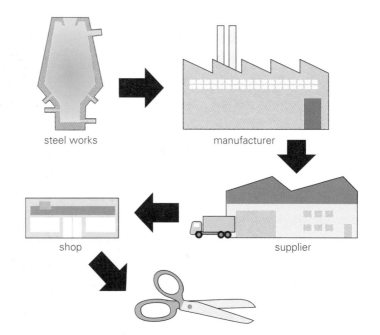

steel works   manufacturer

shop   supplier

Where do scissors come from?

These jewels and the gold came out of the Earth.

Minerals and ores

Minerals are the useful parts of rocks. So coal, oil and limestone are all minerals. They can be elements like pure gold, or compounds like sand. Many minerals are mined and used just as they are, like sand for making concrete and bricks, or clay in pottery. Other minerals, like iron ore, need digging out of the ground and then need chemical processing before they are used.

All of our metals come from the Earth. Most are joined to non-metal elements, especially oxygen. The part of a mineral rock which is useful to us is called an **ore**. The difficult task in getting metals from ores is pulling the metal element away from the non-metal.

Minerals are mined from the Earth.

Metal ore	Name	Compound
aluminium	bauxite	aluminium oxide
iron	haematite	iron oxide
lead	galena	lead sulphide

If you look back at the history of the world, you would see how the discovery of new materials has affected the way people live. Stone age men had no bicycles, partly because they had no metals. Nelson could not use nuclear weapons against Napoleon, because pure uranium had not been separated. Early computers filled whole rooms until the silicon produced was pure enough to manufacture smaller computer chips.

All sorts of minerals came from all sorts of rocks.

QUESTIONS

1   Match these pairs:

   oxygen ⎫   ⎧ sea
   salt   ⎬ from the ⎨ air
   iron   ⎭   ⎩ earth

2   Put the following materials into the two groups: **a** and **b**

   **coal   iron ore   gold   bauxite
   sand   gravel   clay   galena**

   a materials that are useful as they are dug up

   b materials that need to be processed before they can be used.

3   Choose three objects in your home and say:

   a what they are made from

   b whether the raw materials were obtained from the air, the sea, or rocks.

6.2 Metals from rocks

What is the secret of turning rocks into racing cars?

There are five key stages in getting useful metal out of rocks.

- ▪ *Discovery* – finding the ore in the Earth

- ▪ *Mining* – using explosives, tunnelling or open cast diggers to get the rocks out

- ▪ *Concentrating* – removing the non-useful waste rock to leave the metal ore

- ▪ *Extracting* – getting the metal from the ore

- ▪ *Manufacturing* – turning the raw metal into an object.

A lot of rock has to be dug up to get a little copper.

Starting in the ground

Many ores have only a small amount of metal in them, so huge quantities of rock have to be removed to get enough metal. This means some very big holes on the Earth, not to mention a lot of waste!

Extracting the metal

The task of the chemist is to extract or to pull the metal away from the non-metal in the ore. When oxygen is removed from a substance, that substance is **reduced**.

The tighter a metal holds on to the non-metal, the more difficult it is to extract. Look at the reactivity series again.

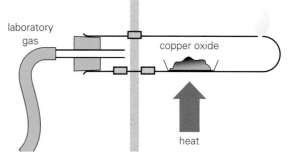

Reducing copper oxide to copper metal.

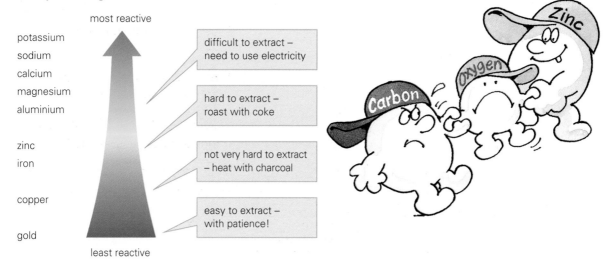

most reactive	
potassium	difficult to extract – need to use electricity
sodium	
calcium	
magnesium	hard to extract – roast with coke
aluminium	
zinc	not very hard to extract – heat with charcoal
iron	
copper	easy to extract – with patience!
gold	
least reactive	

The metals more recently discovered are the ones that are harder to extract. This has influenced history. For example, Concorde couldn't have been invented 200 years ago partly because the way to extract aluminium was unknown.

Discovery and use of common metals		
Metal	Date first known	Main uses
gold	5000BC	jewellery
copper	3000BC Bronze Age	pots, pans
iron	1000BC Iron Age	ploughs, swords
aluminium	1870s	lightweight vehicles and aircraft
uranium	1940s	nuclear power

Despite being rare, gold was discovered long ago because it is easy to extract. Aluminum ore is very common on the Earth, but aluminium metal could not be extracted until electricity was invented. The immense power of the atomic reaction used in power stations and bombs was not possible without pure uranium.

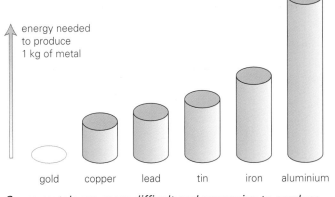

Some metals are more difficult and expensive to produce than others.

The discovery of uranium made nuclear weapons possible.

QUESTIONS

1 Complete the sentences by choosing from the pairs of words:
   a Metals at the top of the activity series are **easy/hard** to obtain.
   b Metal ores are **reduced/oxidised** to make the metal.
   c Mining produces a **lot of/little** waste.

2 Why did the Iron Age come after the Bronze Age?

3 Put these boxes in the right order, to make a flow diagram:

   | waste rock removed | | copper extracted from ore |

   | copper metal made into pipes | | copper ore mined |

KEY IDEAS

Metals are extracted from their ores.

Metals high in the reactivity series are harder to extract.

Metals low down in the reactivity series are easier to extract.

The removal of oxygen from a compound is called reduction.

Mining creates a lot of waste.

6.3 *An ancient and cheap metal*

How do you think the discovery of iron changed people's lives?

Three thousand years ago was a time called the 'Iron Age'. People started to use iron to make swords and ploughs. This changed their simple lives dramatically. Nowadays, Britain produces 10 million tonnes of iron per year.

Iron ore

The main ores are:

■ magnetite (a magnetic rock)

■ haematite or iron oxide (a red rock). (The name haematite begins like the word haemoglobin, which is an iron compound found in the red cells of blood.)

Both ores are turned into the metal iron in a blast furnace.

From iron ... came steel ... came steam trains.

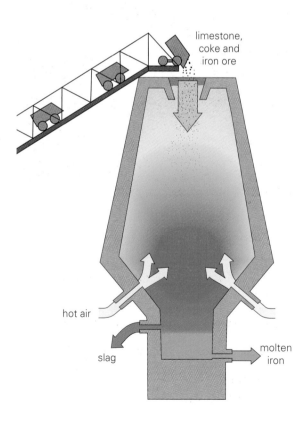

A blast furnace turns iron ore into molten iron.

Ingredients

Iron ore, limestone and coke are put in the furnace, along with blasts of very hot air.

The coke removes the oxygen from the iron oxide ore. This is a reduction reaction (the iron ore is reduced). This is because carbon is more reactive than iron in the reactivity series.

iron oxide + carbon → iron + carbon dioxide
(iron ore)   (coke)

The carbon dioxide formed reacts with more coke to make carbon monoxide. This gas also takes oxygen from the iron oxide ore.

The limestone removes some impurities, mostly the acidic ones. The main impurity is sand or soil from around the ore.

impurity + limestone → slag
(sand)

Iron forms as a red-hot liquid at the bottom and is drained off. The impurities form into slag which is scraped off the surface of the molten iron. Slag is used as a building material.

Molten iron is tapped off from a blast furnace.

The blast furnace

These ingredients are fed into the furnace all day and night. In fact, the process is only stopped to rebuild the furnace walls about every two years. A typical blast furnace is about 70 m high with a tall, thin chimney. It can make up to 7000 tonnes of iron every day.

The molten iron is poured into small moulds. This forms **cast iron**, which is brittle and limited in its use. Carbon and sulphur impurities make it brittle.

Steel

Molten iron is sent to the steel furnace. It is blasted with pure oxygen and limestone, to remove excess carbon. Small amounts of other metals are added to make different steels.

- Chromium increases resistance to rusting, making stainless steel.

- Tungsten makes a tough steel used to coat armoured tanks or to cut other metals.

Steel can be cast into slabs, rolled into sheets or girders, or forged into other shapes by pressing or hammering.

This modern city would not be possible without steel.

QUESTIONS

1 Complete the sentences:
  a Iron ore is **reduced/oxidised** to iron in a _____ furnace.
  b Molten iron is tapped off, and the impurity is removed as _____.
2 List the substances put in to a blast furnace, and the substances taken out.
3 Why is steel more useful than iron?

6.4 *A modern, clean and expensive metal*

In 1893, a statue of Eros was put up in London's Piccadilly Circus. It was cast from pure aluminum – then almost as rare and as expensive as gold!

Posh cutlery

In the 1850s, Napoleon III gave a banquet where his very special guests ate with cutlery made from aluminium. The less important ones managed with gold knives and forks! In those times aluminium was exceedingly rare.

Extracting aluminium

Aluminium ore is called bauxite (aluminium oxide). The aluminium is bound very tightly to the oxygen because it is a reactive metal. Few other elements are able to compete with aluminium for the oxygen. The best way to reduce it is to drag out the oxygen using electricity. As electricity was not used widely until the late 1860s, aluminium was hardly known before then.

Aluminium was once more valuable than gold.

How does electricity do the separating?

Aluminium oxide is made of tiny particles called ions. Aluminium ions have a positive (+) charge. Oxide ions have a negative (–) charge. When the aluminium oxide is melted, the ions can move around. Electricity can pull the ions in opposite directions, separating the aluminium and the oxide.

aluminium oxide → aluminium + oxygen

This process is called **electrolysis**. The electricity is fed into the aluminium oxide using carbon blocks called **electrodes**.

Aluminium oxide does not conduct electricity until it is melted at 2050°C. The mineral cryolite is added to lower the melting point to 900°C. Producing this metal needs a huge amount of energy (an aluminium factory uses as much energy in one day as a typical home uses in $2\frac{1}{2}$ years!). So aluminium is only made in countries with a lot of cheap electricity, such as the hydroelectric power available in North America, Canada and Scotland.

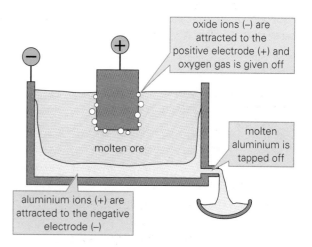

oxide ions (–) are attracted to the positive electrode (+) and oxygen gas is given off

molten ore

molten aluminium is tapped off

aluminium ions (+) are attracted to the negative electrode (–)

Aluminium is made by electrolysis (remember – opposites attract!).

An expensive metal

Aluminium is an expensive metal because of the electrical energy needed to produce it. It has such wonderful properties which make it very useful. It is cheaper and better to **recycle** the metal than to keep making more from the ground. People have recycled milk bottle tops for a long time, but nowadays aluminium cans are often a source of income for environmentally friendly schools.

An aluminium smelter uses lots of energy.

Ideal properties

- Aluminium is reactive in air. It forms a coat of oxide which sticks firmly to the metal surface and protects it from more corrosion.

- It conducts electricity well, so it is used for most of the National Grid overhead cables.

- It has good reflecting properties when polished, so it is used in telescopes and car headlamps.

- It can be rolled thin for sweet wrappers and bottle tops.

- It conducts heat well, so it is used for saucepans.

- It is a lightweight metal which protects itself from corrosion. This is ideal for the bodywork of trains, aircraft and boats.

Aluminium is a very useful metal.

QUESTIONS

1   Complete the sentence:
    Aluminium is extracted from its
    _____ using _____.

2 a List the main properties of aluminium.
  b Now try to give two uses which require that property (e.g. a good conductor of heat = saucepans, cooking foil).

3   Give two reasons why aluminium should be recycled.

6.5 *Getting to know copper*

Coins, cables and copper bottoms – all from this colourful metal. Why is copper so useful?

Copper is useful because of its special properties. It is like other metals, but much better at certain tasks.

Copper bottoms

A 'copper bottomed guarantee' is a promise that will not be broken. The phrase comes from the days of great sailing ships like *HMS Victory*. Hulls were wooden, and covered on the outside with copper. This was to stop certain wood-boring worms making holes in the ship's bottom.

Old ships had copper-covered hulls.

Boring copper?

Copper is very low in the reactivity series. It does very few exciting experiments compared to potassium, because it doesn't react with most chemicals. But this makes it ideally suited to water pipes and tanks, where it doesn't corrode and will not dissolve in water. It is easy to bend and shape, which is helpful for plumbers.

No rust in the bath water with copper pipes!

Good conductor

Copper is an excellent electrical conductor. The purer the copper, the better it conducts. It is used to make electrical wires, and is mixed with zinc to make the brass pins you find in three-pin plugs.

Copper also conducts heat very well, so it is used for saucepans.

Copper is used inside these electrical components.

Wealthy copper

Being unreactive means that copper can be polished and stays quite shiny, so it is used for coins. A penny is now made as an iron disc coated in copper.

Metals are often mixed together to blend their properties. A mixture of metals is called an alloy. Copper is used in different alloys:

- Copper is mixed with gold to harden the gold (and make it a bit cheaper). 24 **carat** gold is pure yet soft, 18 and 9 carat gold have more copper added.

- Brass is an alloy of copper and zinc. Its yellowy colour is between the brown colour of copper and the grey colour of zinc.

- Bronze was one of the earliest known alloys. It is a mixture of tin and copper. Simple bronze tools were found in Iran and Turkey dating back to 4000BC.

Copper is mixed with gold for jewellery.

Obtaining copper

Copper is found in ores such as chalcopyrite – a gold-coloured sulphide. Copper is low in the reactivity series, and so is easy to extract. Copper ore is roasted in air to make the oxide. The oxygen is then taken away with coke. The copper produced this way is not very pure, and may contain precious metals like silver and platinum, so it has to be purified.

QUESTIONS

1 Choose from the pairs to complete the sentences:
Copper is **low/high** in the reactivity series and **easy/hard** to extract from its ore.

2 a List all the properties of copper.
  b Find a use that goes with each property (e.g. good conductor = used for wires).

3 Name two alloys of copper. Say which metal is mixed with copper in each. Give a use for each alloy.

e.g.

Copper alloy	Metal mixed	Use of alloy

KEY IDEAS

Copper is an unreactive metal.

The properties of copper make it very useful.

6.6 *Concrete and glass from rocks*

*How can rock be turned into something runny –
and something you can see through – and end up
in every building around you?*

Natural calcium carbonate

Calcium carbonate is the main chemical
that makes limestone, but it is also the
main chemical in chalk and marble.
Calcium carbonate is made from the shells
of dead sea creatures, decayed over
millions of years. Chalk is found nearest
the surface, limestone is deeper and marble
is deepest.

Limestone

This is one of the most useful rocks on the
Earth. It is used in tarmacadam for road-
making. It is also widely used for other
processes, such as in blast furnaces to make
iron and steel. Powdered limestone is
slightly alkaline, so it is used to neutralise
acidic soil and rivers or lakes affected by
acid rain.

Lime

Heated limestone breaks down to
make lime.

limestone $\rightarrow$ lime + carbon dioxide

$$CaCO_3 \rightarrow CaO + CO_2$$

If you can get it hot enough, lime
glows very brightly. This was used in
theatres to light stages before electric
lighting was invented. You may
have heard the phrase 'being in
the limelight'.

Lime is another useful material. Many
areas have old lime kilns used to
produce lime from limestone, for
farmers to put on their land.

Lime is also used as a cheap alkali. It is
used to make soaps and some fibres.

*Limestone in Derbyshire and the chalk white cliffs of Dover
are made of calcium carbonate.*

Cement

When limestone is heated with clay it produces **cement**. When mixed with sand and water, this runny material reacts slowly but steadily to produce a very hard material used in almost every construction job. **Concrete** is cement, water, sand and gravel mixed together. Sometimes it is **reinforced** with steel to increase its strength.

Glass

Glass is mainly sand, which is heated up and forms a special type of liquid. Soda is added to lower the melting temperature, and limestone is added to stop the glass dissolving in water. Coloured metal oxides are added for green, blue or brown glass.

Modern buildings from ancient rocks!

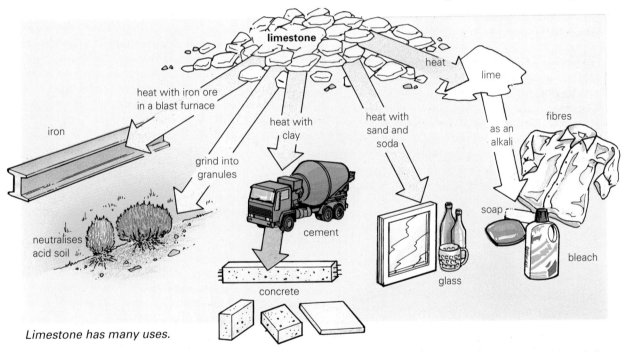

Limestone has many uses.

QUESTIONS

1 Calcium carbonate is found in which three minerals?

2 After an acid leak from a tanker, powdered limestone is put on the road around the spill. Why?

3 The quantity of limestone quarried has risen dramatically in the last 50 years. Which uses do you think might explain this increase?

KEY IDEAS

Limestone is a very useful mineral in building materials, including glass and concrete.

Calcium carbonate is the main chemical in chalk, limestone, and marble.

6.7 Black gold?

Last century, people burned coal for fuel and plastics hadn't been invented, so they didn't use much oil. Now it's one of our most valuable raw materials – but it may run out in your lifetime.

The oil you use today was made millions of years ago. Plants and animals in the sea died, and their remains fell to the sea floor. The remains were squashed down under sand and mud. Bacteria helped them to decompose (break into smaller pieces). This made tiny drops of **crude oil**.

Crude oil is quite a light liquid, so drops move up towards the surface. They pass through **porous** rocks, which have small holes in them like a sponge. The oil stops when it reaches non-porous rock – rock without holes. This traps the oil underneath.

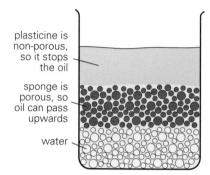

A simple model of underground oil.

Drilling

Oil companies have to find out *where* oil is trapped. Then they drill a hole down through the non-porous rock. When this 'cap' rock is removed, it's like opening a shaken bottle of cola. The oil is suddenly free to escape, and may shoot up the pipes very quickly.

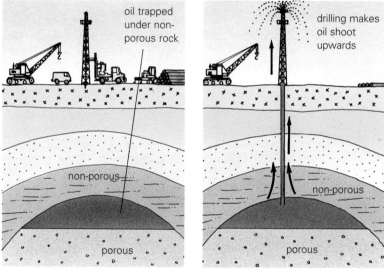

Crude oil is found under non-porous rock.

Crude oil is made from dead plants and animals, and is called a **fossil fuel**. Another fossil fuel is **natural gas**, and is usually found with oil. Both of these fuels are **non-renewable** – they can't be made again. We are using them so quickly that they could run out soon.

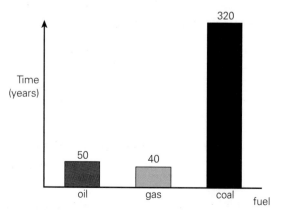

How long will fossil fuels last, if we continue to use them so quickly?

108

Spills and slicks

Oil isn't found in every country, so it has to be moved from place to place. Sometimes pipes are used, but a lot of oil is moved in big ships called tankers.

In 1996, an oil tanker hit some rocks near West Wales, and lots of oil leaked out. This oil formed a slick, or layer, on top of the water. The oil harmed many birds – by sticking in their wings or poisoning them. It also made the beaches very unpleasant.

Why does oil cause these problems?

Two reasons are:

- oil doesn't mix with water
- oil is lighter than water.

So an oil slick floats on top of water and doesn't get broken up very easily.

Waiting for the black tide of destruction

By Charles Clover
Environment Editor

BLACK waves come oozing in at West Angle Bay, down-wind of the crippled Sea Empress oil tanker at anchor in the mouth of Milford Haven waterway, where there is a dizzying smell of petrol.

The 6,000 tons of oil that the holed vessel is estimated to have spilled when she ran aground have spread into a slick almost 20 miles square.

For the moment, the prevailing north-west wind   to be   the

The major worry is that the Sea Empress, presently held off the rocks by three tugs, could be holed further if weather conditions worsen.

The Spread of the Slick ...
Haverfordwest
Milford Haven
Sea Empress
Pembroke

'On a clear day you can see the sea from here'

QUESTIONS

1 Complete the sentences, using these words:

   rock   plants   drilling   upwards

   Oil was made millions of years ago from dead _____ and animals.

   The oil then moved _____ until it reached a non-porous _____.

   Oil companies get the oil out by _____.

2 a Why are oil and natural gas called fossil fuels?

   b Look at the bar chart. Work out in which year each fuel may run out.

3 Give three reasons why oil slicks can cause problems. Try to explain your answers.

6.8 *Helpful hydrocarbons*

Crude oil isn't much use as it is found. But it can provide many important substances – if you can separate them from each other.

Crude oil is not just one substance. In other words, it's not pure. It's a mixture of a number of substances. Each substance has a different boiling point, so distillation can be used to separate them.

In distillation, the mixture of different liquids is heated so that they boil and turn into gas. Each gas is then cooled down, and turns back into a liquid. By heating oil slowly, the substances boil and cool one at a time.

The oil has been split into lots of different **fractions**, so this separation is known as **fractional distillation.**

Many of the fractions are used as **fuels**, like petrol and diesel. They burn and give out heat energy. Some of the others don't burn very well, but are useful for making other chemicals, such as plastics and detergents.

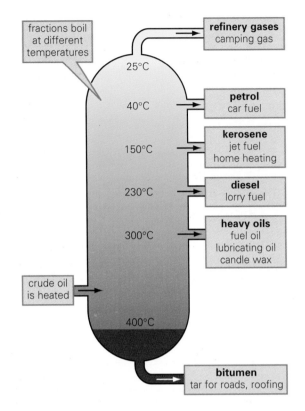

fractions boil at different temperatures

25°C → **refinery gases** camping gas

40°C → **petrol** car fuel

150°C → **kerosene** jet fuel home heating

230°C → **diesel** lorry fuel

300°C → **heavy oils** fuel oil lubricating oil candle wax

crude oil is heated →

400°C

→ **bitumen** tar for roads, roofing

Crude oil can be separated into useful substances.

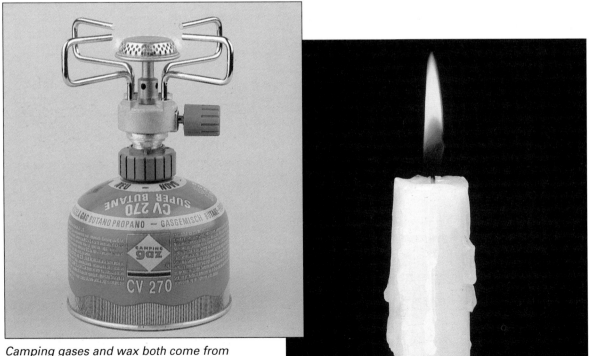

Camping gases and wax both come from crude oil.

Hydrocarbons

All of the substances in crude oil are **hydrocarbons**. This means that they are compounds made from the elements carbon and hydrogen joined together.

The difference between these compounds is the size of their molecules. (Remember, a molecule is a group of atoms joined together.) The formula of each compound tells you how many atoms are in a molecule.

A molecule from diesel ($C_{18}H_{38}$) is much bigger than a natural gas molecule (CH_4).

Hydrocarbons with small molecules boil at a lower temperature than hydrocarbons with larger molecules. In the fractional distillation of oil, the different fractions always boil off in the same order, as the temperature gets higher. Small molecules are collected first.

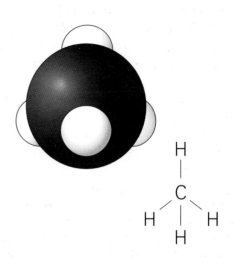

A molecule of natural gas (CH_4) shown in two different ways.

A molecule from diesel ($C_{18}H_{38}$).

QUESTIONS

1   Complete the sentences using these words:

   carbon   distillation   mixture   boils
   liquid   hydrocarbon

   Crude oil is a _____ of different substances. Each substance is a _____. This means it is a compound containing _____ and hydrogen joined together.

   Crude oil is separated by fractional _____. It is heated so that each substance _____ and is then cooled, so that it turns back to a _____.

2   Use the main diagram to suggest the boiling temperature of each fraction:
   a diesel **b** refinery gases **c** bitumen
   d petrol **e** kerosene.

KEY IDEAS

Crude oil is a mixture of different hydrocarbon compounds.

Crude oil is separated by fractional distillation.

Some hydrocarbons are good fuels. Others are used to manufacture useful chemicals.

Compounds with small molecules boil before compounds with big molecules.

6.9 *Comparing hydrocarbons*

You can't heat your home with bitumen, or lubricate a car engine with camping gas. So what makes the hydrocarbons in crude oil different?

Debbie and Satoshi are training to be mechanics at college. Their first task is to find the differences between petrol, diesel and lubricating oil (used to make engines run smoothly).

'All three are liquids found in crude oil, so they must all be hydrocarbons,' says Debbie. Satoshi goes to the library to do some research, and finds the information in this table.

Satoshi's notes include some important ideas.

- Petrol has the smallest molecules, and boils (or evaporates) most easily.

- Lubricating oil has the biggest molecules, and is the hardest to boil.

They decide to carry out two experiments, to get more information.

	number of carbon atoms in each molecule	boiling point
petrol	6 - 9	40°C
diesel	16 - 22	230°C
lubricating oil	30 - 32	305°C

Satoshi's information.

Runniness

Debbie puts each liquid into a container, and times how long it takes to run through a tube into a measuring cylinder. To make it a fair test, she uses the same volume of each liquid, and the same size tube.

From the results, Debbie can tell that petrol is the runniest liquid, because it was the fastest to flow. Lubricating oil is the least runny.

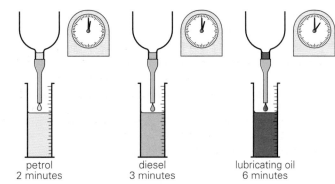

petrol
2 minutes

diesel
3 minutes

lubricating oil
6 minutes

Debbie compares the runniness of liquids.

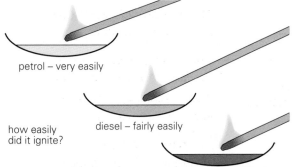

petrol – very easily

how easily did it ignite?

diesel – fairly easily

lubricating oil – difficult

Satoshi compares how easily the liquids burn.

Flammability

Satoshi sets up a fair test to see how easily each liquid will burn. He uses the same amount of liquid each time. (To be safe, he only uses small amounts.) He holds a lighted splint above the surface, until the liquid catches alight.

His results show that petrol is most flammable – it catches alight most easily. Lubricating oil is the hardest to light.

Satoshi and Debbie can see a pattern in the results from their investigation.

Debbie and Satoshi's conclusion.

This hydrocarbon fuel was very flammable.

Alkanes

The hydrocarbons in crude oil are part of a 'family' of hydrocarbons called the **alkanes**. Each member of this family has a name ending in *-ane*. The rest of the name tells you how many carbon atoms are in each molecule.

Each compound also has a chemical formula. The formula tells you how many carbon and hydrogen atoms are in a molecule of that compound.

Alkane molecules		
Name	**Size**	**Formula**
methane	1 carbon	CH_4
ethane	2 carbons	C_2H_6
propane	3 carbons	C_3H_8
butane	4 carbons	C_4H_{10}

QUESTIONS

1   Use the words **more** or **less** to complete these sentences:

   a Petrol is _____ runny then diesel.

   b Lubricating oil is _____ runny then diesel.

   c Petrol is _____ flammable than lubricating oil.

2   At a garage, petrol and diesel are often spilt on the ground. Which one would disappear first? Explain your choice.

3   Octane is an alkane with 8 carbons. Decane is an alkane with 10 carbons.

   In what ways would decane and octane be different?

KEY IDEAS

The compounds in oil have different size molecules.

Hydrocarbons with small molecules are easier to boil, burn and pour, than those with big molecules.

Alkanes are a family of hydrocarbon substances.

6.10 *Better safe than sorry*

How can one oxygen atom make the difference between safe heat and deadly gas?

When a substance burns and reacts with oxygen, heat energy is released. This chemical reaction is called combustion.

In a Bunsen burner, methane gas is burnt (combusted). Methane is a hydrocarbon (formula CH_4). During combustion, oxygen combines with carbon and hydrogen from the methane. This makes two new substances – carbon dioxide (CO_2) and water (H_2O). You can show this in a word equation.

methane + oxygen $\rightarrow$ carbon dioxide + water

Burning *any* hydrocarbon will make carbon dioxide and water.

During the reaction the elements in methane have joined with oxygen. This shows that combustion is also an example of an oxidation reaction.

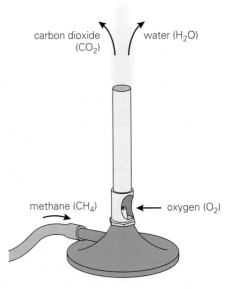

Methane burns completely in plenty of oxygen.

You can't see the carbon dioxide or water produced when you burn methane. So how do you know they are there? Here are two tests you could do.

■ Pass the gases produced over a piece of cobalt chloride paper. Water vapour will turn the paper from blue to pink.

■ Bubble the gases produced through some lime water. Carbon dioxide will turn the lime water cloudy.

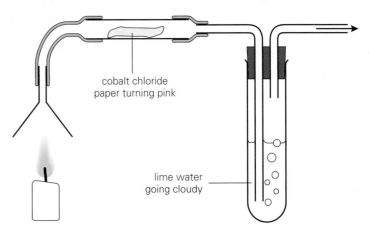

You can prove that candle wax is a hydrocarbon by testing the gases produced.

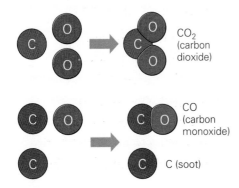

Less oxygen means less carbon dioxide.

Not enough oxygen?

Many people die at home each year, poisoned by their gas heaters. It's not methane that kills them – it's a gas called carbon monoxide.

During combustion, every carbon atom joins with two oxygen atoms to make carbon dioxide (CO_2). But if a burning fuel can't get enough oxygen, each carbon joins with only one oxygen atom – making carbon monoxide (CO). Some carbon may get no oxygen at all to join with – this is what makes soot.

Less oxygen makes a yellow, sooty flame.

A blue flame means safer, complete combustion.

Burning without enough oxygen is called incomplete combustion. You can see it on a Bunsen burner. A closed air-hole lets in less oxygen. The flame turns yellow and will leave more soot. There will also be more carbon monoxide – but you can't see it.

Carbon monoxide has no colour or smell, but if you breathe in too much it can kill you. It's very important that gas heaters are serviced regularly, to check that they can get enough oxygen. You could also buy a carbon monoxide alarm – it could save your life.

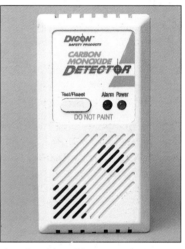

An alarm could stop carbon monoxide from killing.

QUESTIONS

1   Complete these sentences:
   a Combustion is a reaction where a fuel burns and combines with _____ .
   b Burning a hydrocarbon makes two substances – _____ _____ and _____ .
   c With less oxygen, combustion may also make soot and a poisonous gas called _____ _____ .

2   How could you test a gas to see if it was
   a carbon dioxide
   b water?

3   Car engines burn hydrocarbons called petrol or diesel. Why is it dangerous to keep a car engine running inside a closed garage?

6.11 What's in the cracker?

Plastics don't grow on trees, or come out of the ground. They have to be made, using chemicals from crude oil.

In 1863 there was a shortage of ivory. This was a big problem for a company in the USA, who used ivory to make pool balls. So they offered $10 000 to anyone who could invent another substance for making the balls. Wesley Hyatt tried to do it – and made the world's first **plastic**. (Sadly, it got soft when warmed. So it wasn't used for pool balls – and Hyatt didn't get the money!)

The first plastic wasn't quite right for pool balls.

Which bit of oil?

After oil has been distilled, some of the fractions are sold straight away. Petrol and diesel are used as fuels in cars and lorries. There is a huge demand for petrol and diesel.

But there is less demand for some other fractions. They aren't used as fuels, as they don't burn very well. This is because they contain very big molecules.

So the big molecules are broken into smaller molecules. This process is called **cracking**. The big molecules are heated inside a piece of equipment called a cracker. (A substance called a catalyst is added, to speed up the change.)

Cracking uses heat to turn unpopular hydrocarbons into more useful hydrocarbons. This reaction is an example of thermal decomposition. (*Thermal* means heat is used, *decomposition* means something breaks into smaller bits.)

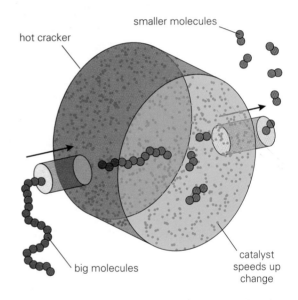

Cracking breaks up big molecules into smaller molecules.

Making a plastic

After cracking, you have lots of useful small molecules. A common one is called ethene. It has the formula C_2H_4. What can you do with ethene?

- Use it as a fuel. It burns well – but you already have lots of good fuels.

- Use it to make plastics. Ethene molecules can be joined together in a long chain, called a **polymer**. There can be millions of ethene molecules in each chain. The polymer is a new substance called poly(ethene). This is an important plastic, whose name is often shortened to polythene. (*Poly* means 'lots of', so poly(*ethene*) means 'lots of ethenes'.)

Most plastics are produced like this – making long polymer chains from small molecules. The name tells you which small molecule was used.

- polystyrene
  = lots of styrenes

- polypropene
  = lots of propenes

- poly vinylchloride (PVC)
  = lots of vinylchlorides

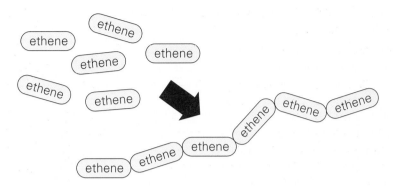

Making a polymer chain.

Polythene and PVC are both made from oil.

QUESTIONS

1 Join up each plastic with the small molecule it is made from:

polystyrene   propene
polyethene   styrene
polypropene   ethene

2 Draw a diagram to show how polystyrene is made from lots of styrene molecules. Use Ⓢ for a styrene molecule.

3 a What happens during cracking?

  b Why is cracking sometimes described as thermal decomposition?

KEY IDEAS

Big molecules are broken into small molecules by cracking.

Plastics are made by joining small molecules together into long chains.

6.12 *Wonderful plastics*

Could you imagine a world without plastics? In the last 40 years, they have completely changed the way we live.

Plastics have given designers a new material to use alongside wood, metals, fabrics and even concrete. There are many types of plastics, but they have similar properties:

- lightweight
- good insulators of electricity
- do not corrode or rot very easily
- easily shaped or cut
- quite cheap
- easy to make brightly coloured.

For example, polythene is used for carrier bags and cable insulation, PVC is used for guttering and plastic seat covers.

Look around at all the plastic items in your school and home. Pens and rulers, drinks bottles, chairs and bags, maybe the window frames. The wide range of cheap bright toys young children play with were not even made 40 years ago.

New inventions

The special properties of plastics have made many new inventions possible from CDs to trainers. Personal stereos are lightweight compared to early radios. New plastics are fire-resistant. Some make bullet-proof vests five times stronger than steel. A plastic engine has been developed for racing cars which is less than half the weight of a normal engine.

How good were the 'Good Old Days'?

Plastics are strong but light.

Fabrics

Plastics like nylon, polyester and terylene are all made from crude oil. Fabric materials used in clothes and carpets all contain chemicals called polymers.

Using up all the oil?

Oil takes millions of years to form, but only a few hundred years to use up. We must be careful how much we use. If we run short of oil, plastics will become very expensive. Plastic objects could be replaced by traditional materials like wood, as trees can be replaced quicker than oil. Fewer man-made fibres would mean returning to wool or cotton.

Rubbish

Most plastics do not break down or rot in the environment. This can be useful. For example, double-glazed PVC window frames do not need replacing or painting. But where do you put plastics at the end of their life? As they do not rot, they create a lot of litter. Look outside – there are probably some crisp packets blowing about.

Recycling

Recycling is very difficult with plastics. There are so many different sorts you might need 20 different bins. Few people can be bothered to sort out every type of plastic. Some factories producing a lot of plastic waste recycle it, like milk crate manufacturers.

In some areas, recycling bags are collected separately with household rubbish.

Plastics are used to make synthetic fibres for clothes.

Plastic causes a major litter problem.

QUESTIONS

1   Rearrange these phrases to make a sentence:

fibres and plastics	chemicals to make
as a source of	items like
We depend	on crude oil

2   Match the plastic object with the reason for its use:

window frame	bright colour
cable cover	lightweight
toy	insulator
carrier bag	rustproof

3   Write three sentences about what life would be like without plastics.

KEY IDEAS

Plastics have very useful properties.

Plastics have changed our lives.

Plastics are difficult to recycle.

119

6.13 *Making a car*

This chapter has looked at harvesting materials from the Earth. To summarise this, look at how some materials from the Earth are used to make a car.

Metals and other materials

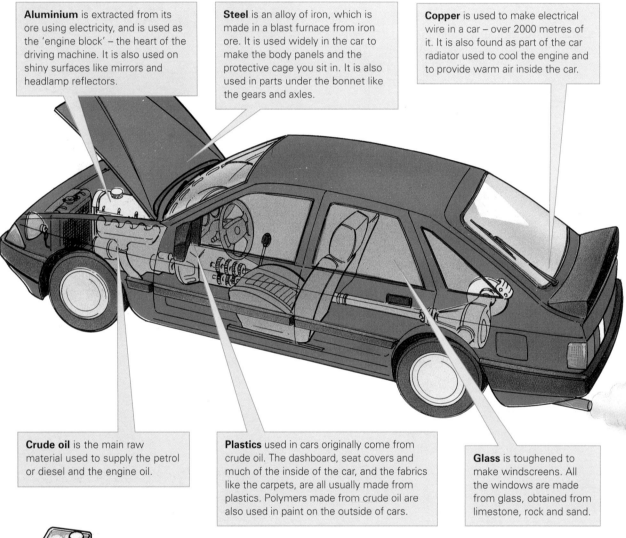

Aluminium is extracted from its ore using electricity, and is used as the 'engine block' – the heart of the driving machine. It is also used on shiny surfaces like mirrors and headlamp reflectors.

Steel is an alloy of iron, which is made in a blast furnace from iron ore. It is used widely in the car to make the body panels and the protective cage you sit in. It is also used in parts under the bonnet like the gears and axles.

Copper is used to make electrical wire in a car – over 2000 metres of it. It is also found as part of the car radiator used to cool the engine and to provide warm air inside the car.

Crude oil is the main raw material used to supply the petrol or diesel and the engine oil.

Plastics used in cars originally come from crude oil. The dashboard, seat covers and much of the inside of the car, and the fabrics like the carpets, are all usually made from plastics. Polymers made from crude oil are also used in paint on the outside of cars.

Glass is toughened to make windscreens. All the windows are made from glass, obtained from limestone, rock and sand.

Crude oil is also used in some of the materials for brake fluids, antifreeze in the radiator and the screen wash.

Making pollution, too

Cars produce fumes from the engine. These can be harmful and damage the environment.

This problem has been solved partly by chemists designing catalysts, placed in the exhaust pipes. These remove some of the gases by getting them to react together to make less harmful gases.

carbon dioxide – a greenhouse gas

carbon monoxide – a poisonous gas

lead fumes – another poison

nitrogen oxides – acid fumes

hydrocarbon fumes – possibly harmful

A catalytic converter can reduce harmful gases from exhaust fumes.

Environmentally responsible

Most cars end up on the scrap heap sooner or later. What happens to all the metals, plastics and glass? Scrap yards take off some parts to be used again, but others just rot away.

Cars are now being produced with a view to reclaiming and recycling. The glass, steel and some plastics can be removed more easily, melted and reused.

Parts like fuel tanks are being made from plastics which can be completely recycled.

QUESTIONS

1 Match the item with the original material it came from:

windscreen	iron ore
fuel	crude oil
door panel	crude oil
seat	limestone/sand

2 **a** Choose any two everyday objects (a bicycle, drill, computer, etc.) and draw simple diagrams of them, or cut a picture from an old magazine.

 b Identify the materials used to make each object (e.g. steel, plastic, glass).

 c Complete a table for where the materials originally came from:

Material	Origin
plastic	crude oil

KEY IDEAS

Objects are made from materials harvested from the world around us.

Chemistry provides some ways of dealing with pollution.

Recycling is better than leaving materials to corrode or rot.

7.1 *Non-stop Earth*

The land underneath you looks very still, but the Earth's surface is actually moving and changing all the time.

These photographs show changes in the Earth's surface. The railway collapsed because of sudden shaking movements inside the Earth. We call this an **earthquake**. The hotel collapsed when the cliff slipped into the sea. Waves wore away rocks in the cliff for many years, until the cliff was too weak to stay up.

These movements happened suddenly, and were very dangerous to people nearby. You may see similar examples on television. But most changes happen very slowly, and never make the news.

An earthquake in Japan caused lots of damage.

Weathering and erosion

Mountains, cliffs and rocks are all being worn down and changed by a process called **erosion**. It can be caused by many things – the most common one being the weather. We call this process **weathering**.

Weathering and erosion happen in different ways:

- Wind blows away small pieces of rock.

- Waves break bits of rock off cliffs.

- Flowing water wears away rock in its path.

- Rain water dissolves some types of rock.

- Water in rocks freezes. This makes the water expand, so it cracks the rock.

- Acids in rain react with some rocks, e.g. limestone.

- Roots of trees make cracks in rocks as they grow.

A collapsing cliff in Yorkshire brought an end to this hotel.

water at room temperature   below 0°C inside a freezer

Water expands when it freezes, and cracks the bottle.

122

Where do all the bits go?

When bits of rock break off, they get moved to another place. Usually, streams and rivers carry the bits of rock down to the sea. The rocks are dumped onto the sea floor.

As rocks are moved, they may rub against the edge of the river. The banks and floor get worn down by this – another example of erosion.

The Earth's surface is always being eroded. You play a small part in this. For example, walking or cycling on popular paths in the countryside can cause erosion of the ground.

The river has worn away a lot of this rock.

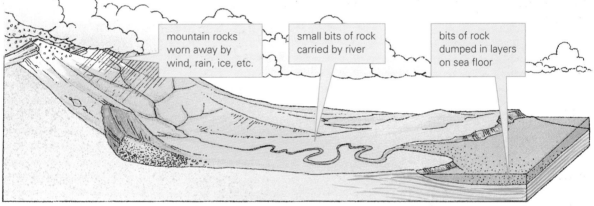

mountain rocks worn away by wind, rain, ice, etc.

small bits of rock carried by river

bits of rock dumped in layers on sea floor

Rocks from mountains end up on the sea floor.

QUESTIONS

1 Choose the correct name from this list to match each description:

   earthquake   waves   expands   weathering

   a water gets bigger when it turns to ice

   b the Earth's surface moves suddenly and violently

   c mountains are worn away by wind and rain

   d a cliff is worn away by being hit by these.

2 How do humans erode the land? Suggest five different ways.

3 You find a rock on a beach. It has come from a high mountain 100 miles inland. Explain how the rock got to the beach.

KEY IDEAS

The surface of the Earth is always changing.

Large bits of rock are broken into smaller pieces by things like wind, rain, waves and ice. This is called erosion.

Pieces of rock are carried to the sea floor by streams and rivers.

7.2 Stick them together again

Weathering and erosion dump millions of tiny bits of rock on the sea floor. What happens to them?

Making new rocks

The tiny pieces of rock dumped on the sea floor are called sediments. Each layer of sediment will have more sediment dumped on top. Over many thousands and millions of years, the sediments will be pressed together very tightly. This pressure makes them stick together to form new rock – called **sedimentary** rock.

Like sediment layers, the one at the bottom is under most pressure.

Tiny animals and plants in the sea also fall to the sea floor when they die. They get squashed into rocks with the sediments. The remains of these creatures from thousands of years ago are known as **fossils**. You can often see fossils in sedimentary rocks. Scientists have worked out when these creatures lived, and can use fossils to tell how old a rock is.

Sedimentary rocks you might come across include limestone, sandstone and mudstone.

Limestone is made from shells and skeletons of dead sea-creatures.

Sandstone is made from grains of sand.

Mudstone is made from tiny rock particles, smaller than sand grains.

Sedimentary rocks are made in layers. It's like making a bed – each new layer goes on top of the previous layer. The oldest rocks will be lower down (like the underblanket), and the top layer will contain the newest rocks (like the top blanket or bedspread).

The layers get older as you go down.

Folding

Sometimes, earth movements squeeze a section of rock from both ends. The rock is pushed up. This is called **folding**. The land rises in places, making mountains and valleys. The Alps in Europe, the Rockies in America and the Himalayas in Asia were all made in this way.

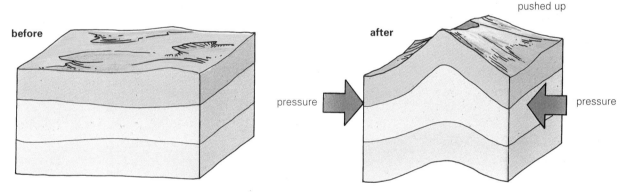

Pressure from the sides makes a mountain rise up.

QUESTIONS

1 Complete these sentences:

a _____ rocks are usually made under the sea floor.

b Tiny bits of rock join together under high _____.

c _____ are made if dead animals are trapped in the rocks.

2 Look at the diagram showing some layers of rock. Which rock is the oldest? Explain why you chose this one.

3 The Earth's highest mountain, Everest, is in the Himalayas. The rocks at the top are sedimentary, and could contain fossils of sea animals. How did they get there?

KEY IDEAS

Sedimentary rocks are made by squeezing together small bits of rock.

Sedimentary rocks contain fossils, grains and layers.

Mountains can be formed by folding.

7.3 *Cool it and make it*

Not all rocks are sedimentary. You need to dig deep to find out why!

Rocks like granite and basalt are very different from sedimentary rocks. They don't contain fossils or grains of sediment, and don't have layers within them. Instead, they are made up of crystals. They are given the name **igneous** rocks.

If you go down a mine, you find that it gets hotter as you go deeper. If you go much further down than the deepest mine, it gets so hot that rocks melt. The liquid rock deep inside the Earth is called **magma**.

This hot magma will turn back into solid rock if it cools down. Sometimes it rises slowly inside the Earth, getting cooler and cooler, and gradually becomes solid. This slow cooling makes a solid with large crystals – like granite.

Earth's deepest mine (South Africa) about 3.5 km

Granite is made by slow cooling.

Basalt is made by fast cooling.

At other times, hot magma shoots out of volcanoes as **lava**. The air on the surface of the Earth is much colder than inside the Earth, so the lava cools down much more quickly. This makes rocks with much smaller crystals – like basalt.

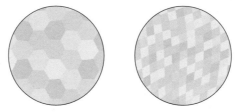

Crystals formed slowly ... and quickly.

depth of Earth's crust about 40 km

mantle (magma found here)

Magma is a long way down!

Inside the Earth

Nobody has been very far inside the Earth, but studying rocks and earthquakes has helped scientists to work out what it must be like.

It's a bit like an egg that is nearly hard-boiled! You walk around on the 'shell'.

- There's a central **core**, which is very hot and mainly liquid.

- Outside the core is the **mantle** – mainly solid, except for liquid magma near the surface.

- The thin outside layer is called the **crust**. It is mainly covered by sea.

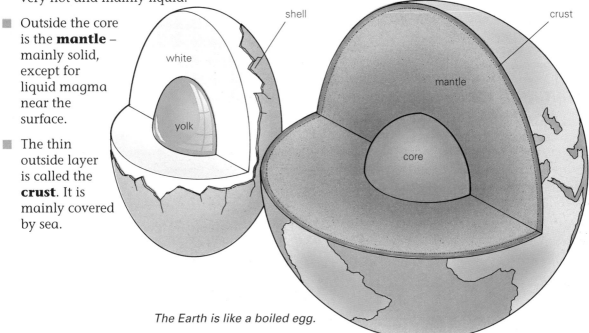

The Earth is like a boiled egg.

QUESTIONS

1 Choose the correct word from these to match each description:

   lava   igneous   magma

   a hot liquid rock inside the Earth

   b liquid rock coming out from a volcano

   c rock that is made by cooling hot liquids.

2 Granite is made by magma cooling slowly. Basalt is made by magma cooling much faster. How will the two rocks look different?

3 The Earth is sometimes said to be like a boiled egg. Link the parts of the egg with matching parts of the Earth.

yolk	crust
shell	mantle
white	core

7.4 *All change*

The recipe for marble is simple. Take some limestone. Heat under pressure for several million years ...

In 1806, Sir James Hall heard that limestone could change to marble. He wanted to find out how. So he filled a gun barrel with limestone powder, and blocked both ends. He then put the gun into a hot oven. When he opened the gun later, he found that heat and pressure inside the gun *had* changed the limestone into crystals of marble.

Changing rocks

Rocks like marble are called **metamorphic**. They are made when one type of rock is heated and squashed very strongly, deep inside the Earth. The new rock is very different from the original rock. It is often harder.

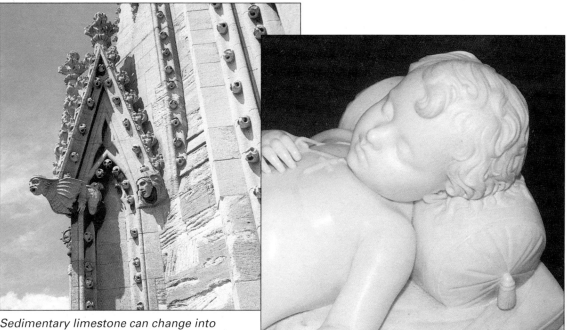

Sedimentary limestone can change into metamorphic marble.

Slate is another metamorphic rock. It is made when mudstone is changed by heating and squashing inside the Earth.

Old rock	Metamorphic rock
limestone →	marble
mudstone →	slate

128

The rock cycle

If you pick up a rock, it will be one of three types –
sedimentary, igneous or metamorphic. But any bit of that rock
could have been part of another type of rock in the past.

It's easier to understand this using a diagram, known as the
rock cycle. It shows how bits of rock can change, and go
round and round (like a cycle). But remember – this takes
millions of years to happen.

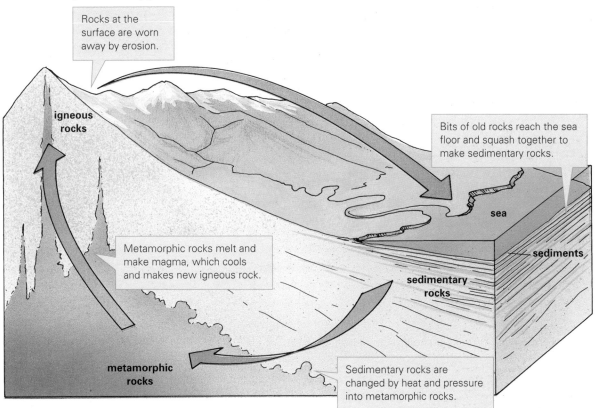

Rocks at the surface are worn away by erosion.

igneous rocks

Bits of old rocks reach the sea floor and squash together to make sedimentary rocks.

sea

Metamorphic rocks melt and make magma, which cools and makes new igneous rock.

sediments

sedimentary rocks

metamorphic rocks

Sedimentary rocks are changed by heat and pressure into metamorphic rocks.

QUESTIONS

1   Complete these sentences:
   a Limestone is a _____ rock which is changed into a metamorphic rock called _____.

   b _____ is a sedimentary rock which changes into a _____ rock called slate.

2   What conditions are needed to make a metamorphic rock?

3   Use the rock cycle to explain how a metamorphic rock could be changed into a sedimentary rock.

7.5 Need a new map?

If aliens in a spaceship had gone past the Earth 50 million years ago, the Earth would have looked very different from how it looks today. What has changed?

Mark lives in Birmingham. He finds a fossil in his garden. It contains a piece of coral. This fossil is a clue that continents have moved.

Coral lives in the sea – but only in warm tropical seas (near the equator, for example). If coral remains are found in the UK, it means that the UK must have been underwater and nearer the equator millions of years ago. Since then, the land has moved. So Birmingham, and Mark's garden, isn't tropical any more!

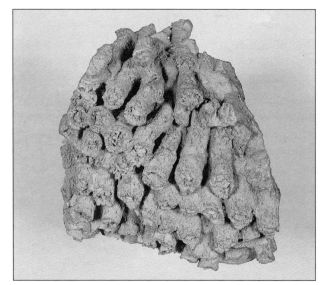

A coral fossil could only have been made in warm tropical water.

Moving continents

In 1910, a German scientist called Alfred Wegener spotted clues like Mark's coral. He suggested that continents had moved. We now think that many continents – like Africa, South America and Australia – were joined together in one piece. They have slowly moved apart.

What are the other clues?

■ The shapes of the continents

This diagram shows how the shapes of the continents could have fitted together.

How it used to be.

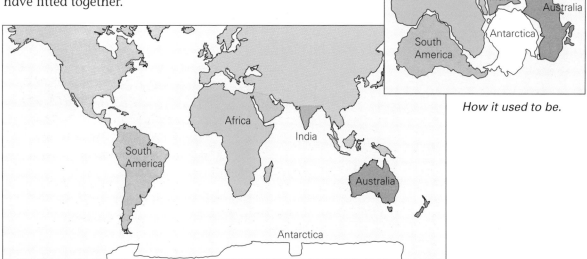

How it looks today.

■ Similar rocks

Scientists went to cliffs and beaches in America and Britain that could have been joined together. They found similar rocks and fossils in both places.

■ Similar animals

In Europe we have reindeer, but in America they have caribou. These two animals are very similar. How could they have travelled across the ocean, from one continent to the other? Perhaps their ancestors were the same, but got separated when the continents moved apart.

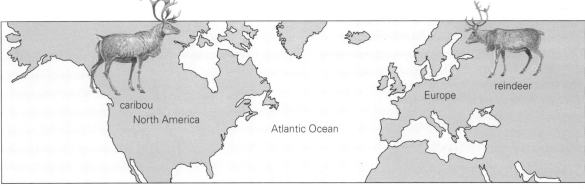

These animals have been separated by water.

■ Coal at the south pole

Coal is a sedimentary rock, made in hot swamps. But coal has been found near the south pole, where it's very cold. The land must have moved there from a warmer place.

Still drifting

The continents are *still* moving apart – but very slowly. They travel at about the same speed as your fingernails grow!

QUESTIONS

1 Complete this sentence.
   Coral lives in warm _____. When it dies it falls to the _____ and gets squashed into sedimentary rocks. This makes a _____ in the rock.

2 Africa's west coast is moving at a speed of 3 cm each year. How far will it travel during the next 6 years?

3 Samantha doesn't believe that America and Europe were once joined together. Write a short letter to explain to her why you think these continents were once joined.

7.6. *Sitting in the middle of a plate*

In Britain, we don't suffer from large earthquakes and volcanoes. Other places aren't so lucky. Why is this?

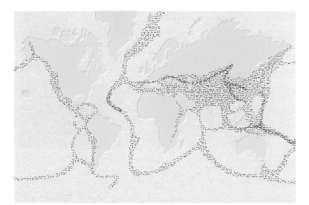

The dots show major earthquakes in the world.

The triangles show major volcanoes in the world.

The two maps above show where most of the big earthquakes or volcanoes have happened. You can see that they don't happen everywhere. Some places have a lot, and others none.

Scientists examining the ocean floor in 1963 found the reason for this pattern. The crust of the Earth is made up of big sections called **plates**. Plates move very slowly. They carry the land we live on – the continents. The plates are like a conveyor belt, carrying the land along.

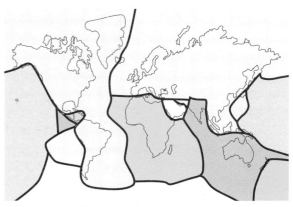

The Earth's surface is made up of sections called plates.

The three maps show you that most earthquakes and volcanoes happen where two plates meet – **plate boundaries**. There are two types of plate boundary:

- where plates move apart

- where plates collide (meet head on).

Plates moving apart

In the middle of the ocean floors, plates move away from each other. Hot liquid magma pours out through the gap from inside the Earth. It cools and makes new igneous rock. This new rock is pushed away from the opening by the next bit of new rock.

This diver is filming lava as it comes out between ocean plates

Plates colliding

When plates move towards each other they collide. This makes the land on top shake – there is an earthquake. One plate is pushed downwards under the other one.

The plate that goes down into the Earth gets hotter. This makes it melt, forming lots of magma. If all this magma is squashed too tightly, it will escape upwards. This is what makes a volcano erupt.

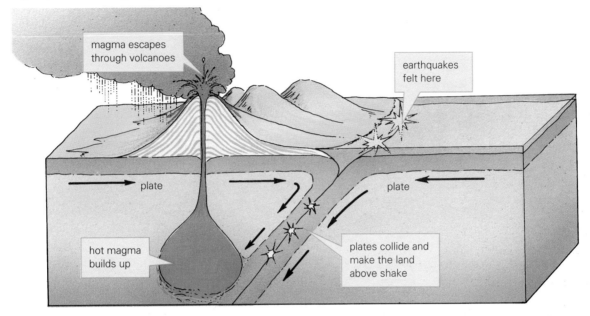

Two plates colliding.

So earthquakes and volcanoes usually happen at places where plates are colliding. Why doesn't Britain have big earthquakes and volcanoes? It's because it is in the *middle* of a plate – a long way from the collisions at the edge.

QUESTIONS

1   From these words, choose the best one to match each description:

    plates   volcano   earthquake   magma

    a a place where hot liquid rock comes out of the Earth
    b the Earth's surface is made of these
    c hot liquid rock under the Earth
    d a violent shaking of the Earth's surface.

2   Earthquakes and volcanoes happen where plates collide. Explain why.

3   Why doesn't Britain suffer from volcanoes and earthquakes?

KEY IDEAS

The Earth's crust is made up of lots of plates.

Plates move and carry continents on top.

New rock is made where plates move apart.

Volcanoes and earthquakes happen where plates collide.

SECTION B: QUESTIONS

1 Here is an outline of the periodic table. Some elements have been marked with letters, though they are *not* the actual symbols of the elements.

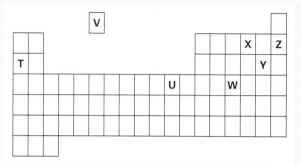

Which letter in this diagram represents the following? (You may use letters more than once.)

i a metal that floats on water
ii a very unreactive gas
iii a substance that forms an ion with a charge of +1
iv a green-coloured gas
v a gas needed for you to breathe
vi the element with the simplest atom
vii a metal which forms coloured compounds
viii a semi-metal.

Use the periodic table on page 175 to answer questions 2, 3 and 4.

2 Caesium has an atomic number of 55.

a What group of the periodic table is it in?

b Name two products you would get when caesium reacts with water.

c What would you expect to see when the caesium is put in the water?

d What would happen to universal indicator put in the water after the reaction?

3 Fluorine has an atomic number of 9.

a How reactive would you expect fluorine to be compared with other non-metals?

b Fluorine reacts with hydrogen to make hydrogen fluoride. Name a common laboratory solution that you expect to behave like hydrogen fluoride solution.

c What two products would you expect to be formed when magnesium reacts with the solution in your answer to **b**?

4 Sulphur has an atomic number of 16.

a Name a gas in the same group as sulphur.

b What charge would a sulphur ion have?

c Sulphur burns in air to make an oxide called sulphur dioxide. Write a word equation for this reaction.

d What sort of solution would be formed when this gas dissolves in water?

e What sort of pollution problem is caused by sulphur dioxide? How might it be overcome?

5 The diagram shows the structure of sodium chloride.

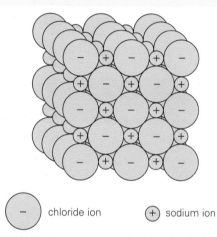

$\ominus$ chloride ion $\oplus$ sodium ion

a How is a chlorine atom different from a chloride ion?

b How is a sodium atom different from a sodium ion?

c Use the diagram to help you explain why:
i a sodium chloride crystal is the shape of a cube
ii it has a high melting point
iii as a solid, it doesn't conduct electricity
iv when melted, it does conduct electricity.

d Magnesium oxide forms a crystal like sodium chloride.
Magnesium is in group 2 of the periodic table. Its atomic number is 12.
Oxygen is in group 6. Its atomic number is 8.
Draw diagrams that show the arrangements of electrons round:
i a magnesium atom
ii a magnesium ion
iii an oxygen atom
iv an oxygen ion.

6 Rosanna wanted to check if lemons were acidic. She squeezed some juice into a test tube and added some universal indicator. The indicator turned yellow.

a Is the pH of lemon juice high or low?

b What is the pH of pure water?

c What colour is universal indicator in water?

d What does the pH value tell Rosanna about lemon juice?

She repeats the experiment with vinegar and the indicator turns red.

e Which is the stronger acid – vinegar or lemon juice?

f Sulphuric acid is an even stronger acid. What hazard code should be seen on bottles of strong acids?

7 The following word equations summarise how sulphuric acid is made.

sulphur   + oxygen → sulphur dioxide

sulphur dioxide + oxygen → sulphur trioxide

sulphur trioxide + water   → sulphuric acid

Use the word equations to help you answer the questions.

a Name an element used to make the acid.

b What is the usual raw material used to obtain oxygen?

c Name one other raw material used in this process.

d The final reaction is very exothermic. What piece of laboratory apparatus would help you to prove this is the case?

8 A large amount of sulphuric acid is used for fertilisers.

ammonia + sulphuric acid → fertiliser X

This is a neutralisation reaction.

a What type of chemical must ammonia be?

b Fertiliser X has the formula $(NH_4)_2SO_4$. What is its chemical name?

c Name the element in this fertiliser which is required by plants.

9 A bike manufacturer is investigating how better to protect bicycles from rust. Steel tubes are placed in three beakers and left for a week.

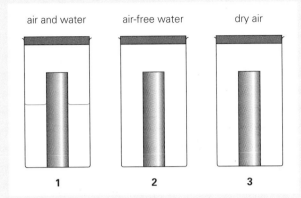

air and water   air-free water   dry air

1   2   3

a Why does the steel tube in jar 2 get no rust?

b Why does the steel tube in jar 3 get no rust?

c Why does the steel tube in jar 1 go rusty?

d Predict what might happen to a steel tube left in salty water, compared to jar 1.

The company decide to paint the bicycle frame to prevent rusting.

e How does painting prevent rust?

f How is a bicycle chain protected from rusting?

10 An underground iron pipe is used to carry water around the streets of a city. It has lumps of scrap magnesium attached along its length, to help prevent rusting.

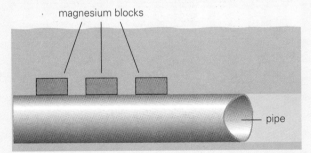

magnesium blocks

pipe

a Is magnesium higher or lower than iron in the reactivity series?

b Magnesium protects the pipe from rusting by sacrificing itself. Use the reactivity series to explain how.

c Suggest another suitable metal from the reactivity series that might protect the pipe.

d Why are the pipes not protected by painting them?

e Plastic pipes are being used when the old iron pipes need replacing. Why?

SECTION B: QUESTIONS

11 The diagram below is a simple carbon cycle.

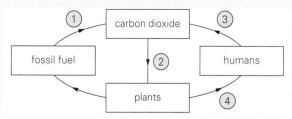

a Name one fossil fuel.

b Choose from the words below to answer the questions which follow.

**combustion   photosynthesis
respiration   eating**

i Which process happens when fuels are burned?

ii Which process reduces the amount of carbon dioxide in the air?

iii Which process links plants to humans?

iv Match each word with a number from the diagram.

c If trees are chopped down and burned, what will happen to the levels of carbon dioxide?

d Carbon dioxide causes global warming. Put the following phrases together in the correct order to explain this idea.

 ■ The Earth is slowly warming up.

 ■ The gas layer traps the heat bouncing off the Earth.

 ■ Sunlight passes through this atmosphere.

 ■ The Earth is surrounded by gases called the atmosphere.

 ■ The light turns to heat as it hits the Earth.

e Suggest one thing that may happen on the Earth if global warming continues.

12 The diagram on the right shows part of the water cycle.

a Match the statements below with the correct numbers on the diagram.

 ■ clouds blown by the wind

 ■ water falling as rain or snow

 ■ clouds forming as water vapour condenses

 ■ heat from the sun evaporating water

 ■ streams and rivers flowing into the sea

b Briefly explain how some water you drink today may get back into your tap in a few years' time.

c By the time a river reaches the sea, most rocks carried by the river have been broken down to sand. Explain why this happens.

13 Mr Jardin puts some tomato plants in a dark shed, and some in his living room.

a After a few days the leaves of the plants in the shed are yellow and dying. Why?

b Some of the plants in the living room are planted in garden soil, some into compost. What is compost?

c The ones in compost grow better than those in soil. Name one chemical element in compost that helps plants grow better.

d He tries to help the plants in the soil by adding a fertiliser called ammonium phosphate ($(NH_4)_3PO_4$). Why might this help the plants recover?

He is so pleased with the chemical fertiliser that he buys some ammonia (NH_3), which is in a common kitchen cleaner. He puts it on the plants. Unfortunately they all die. Mrs Green explains the ammonia is too alkaline for the plants.

e What substance could be added to show ammonia is alkaline?

f What colour would it turn?

g What would ammonia do to the pH of the soil?

Mrs Green suggests the environmentally friendly thing to do with the dead tomato plants is to pile them all up in a bucket and leave them to rot. She suggests this would make a useful material for the future.

h Explain why rotted plants might be useful.

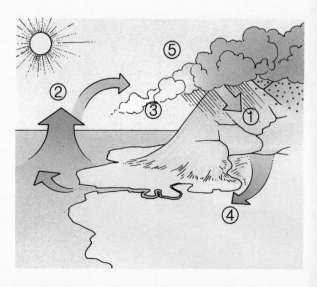

14a The diagram shows a simplified fridge.

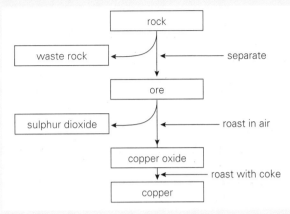

- door seal, casing/body, shelf, plug, motor

   i Why is copper used for the wiring from the plug to the motor?

   ii Why is the body casing made from steel?

   iii Why is the seal on the door made of rubber?

   iv Why are the shelves made from plastic?

b The liquid used inside fridges to cool them down is usually a CFC (chlorofluorocarbon).

   i What damage do CFCs cause to the atmosphere?

   ii What damage might this cause to human life on the Earth?

   iii Suggest one possible solution to this problem.

15 Aluminium has useful properties, but is an expensive metal because it is obtained from its ore (aluminium oxide) using electricity.

a What element other than aluminium is removed by electricity from aluminium ore?

b Why was aluminium rare until the early part of this century?

c Match each use of aluminium with the best reason from those in the lists.

Use
foil wrap on chocolate
aircraft wing
saucepan
overhead electricity cable
window frame
car headlamp reflector

Reason
light but strong
easily highly polished
good conductor of heat
good conductor of electricity
easily made into thin sheets, possibly coloured
does not corrode

d Give two advantages of recycling aluminium.

e Give one reason why more aluminium is not recycled.

16 The chart shows how a metal might be made.

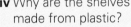

- rock → (separate) → waste rock / ore
- ore → (roast in air) → sulphur dioxide / copper oxide
- copper oxide → (roast with coke) → copper

a What is the name of the product from this process?

b Name three raw materials used in the process.

c Name a substance that is reduced in the process.

d Name a substance that causes oxidation in the process.

e Name one waste product from the process.

f A typical copper ore is only 1% copper. What major environmental problem shown in the diagram does this cause?

g Give two uses for copper.

17 Imagine three metal elements called allium, ballium and callium. Each metal is added in turn to dilute acid. Ballium does nothing, callium fizzes madly, and allium fizzes slowly.

a Put the three in order, from the most reactive to the least reactive.

b Which metal is most likely to carry a hazardous warning?

c Which is likely to be the most useful metal for making a pipe?

d Allium bubbles slowly in cold water and burns in steam. What might callium do in cold water?

e Which metal is likely to be the most difficult to extract from its ore?

f Which metal will corrode the quickest?

g Which metal might have to be kept in a bottle under a layer of oil?

h A nail made from allium is placed in copper sulphate solution. A brown coloured metal coats the nail.
Complete the word equation for this reaction.

allium + copper sulphate

→ _____ _____ + _____

SECTION B: QUESTIONS

18 Complete these sentences.

a Crude oil, coal and natural gas are examples of _____ fuels.

b Compounds containing only carbon and hydrogen are known as _____.

c Petrol and wax are both obtained by separating crude oil. Petrol is a liquid, wax is solid. Petrol contains _____ molecules than wax.

d Plastics contain long chain molecules called _____.

e Carbon monoxide is a toxic gas formed when fuels burn without enough _____.

f You can test to see if a gas is carbon dioxide using _____ _____.

19 Large amounts of natural gas are used in Britain. Most of it is found under the North Sea. Natural gas is a fossil fuel.
The most important chemical in natural gas is methane. Methane is a compound of carbon and hydrogen. It exists as simple molecules shown here in two ways:

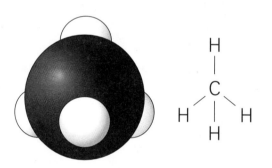

a Why is methane described as a compound?

b Use the diagrams above to write down the chemical formula for methane.

c Explain why natural gas is called a fossil fuel.

d Name another important raw material which is often found underneath natural gas.

e Methane is sometimes turned into a liquid to transport it in tankers. Suggest one advantage of transporting it as a liquid rather than as a gas.

20 If an oil tanker spills oil at sea, it forms an oil slick. This can cause a lot of damage to birds.

a Give two reasons why oil forms a slick on top of the water.

b Suggest two ways in which the oil can harm birds.

21 Inside a camping gas cylinder, propane is stored as a liquid. When the valve is opened, propane turns to a gas and comes out to be burned.

a The diagram shows how propane molecules are arranged as a liquid. Show how propane molecules are arranged as a gas.

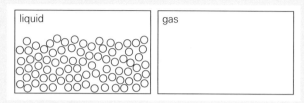

b In which diagram are the molecules moving faster – liquid or gas?

c Complete this word equation for the complete combustion of propane:

propane + oxygen

→ _____ _____ + _____

d Why is this reaction said to be exothermic?

22 Crude oil is separated into fractions by distillation. Some fractions are then *cracked*.

a What conditions are used to carry out cracking?

b What happens to the molecules of a substance when it is cracked?

Ethene is a substance made by cracking. This is then used to make a plastic.

c Complete the diagram to show how ethene molecules Ⓔ join to make a plastic, and name the plastic.

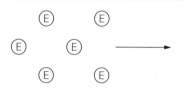

23 Plastics are polymers. Their molecules are long chains made of smaller molecules joined together.

a Complete this table.

Plastic	Small molecule
	ethene
poly(chloroethene)	chloroethene
polystyrene	

b Why is plastic litter more difficult to deal with than some other materials?

138

24 Metals can be joined by welding them together. One way to weld is to use a burner in which acetylene is burned in oxygen. Acetylene is a hydrocarbon (C_2H_2).

a Complete this word equation for the complete combustion of acetylene:

acetylene + oxygen

→ _____ _____ + _____

b If there is a shortage of oxygen, a toxic gas could be made. What is its name?

c Why is the burning of acetylene called an exothermic reaction?

25 These diagrams show how three different rocks appeared when examined under a microscope.

For each one, say whether you think it is an igneous or sedimentary rock, and give one reason for your choice.

a

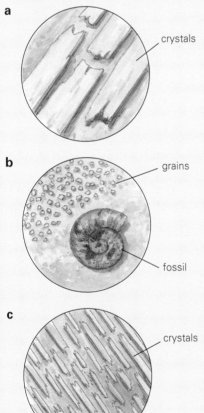

crystals

b

grains

fossil

c

crystals

d Rocks **a** and **c** were both made when liquid rock cooled down. Explain which of these rocks cooled more quickly.

e Another group of rocks are called metamorphic. Explain how these are made.

26 The diagram shows a crack in a piece of rock. The crack has filled with water.

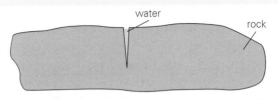

water

rock

Explain why the rock may split if the weather gets very cold.

27a Small pieces of rocks on mountains and cliffs can be broken off by weathering. What type of rock is made when these small fragments are squeezed together?

b This diagram is known as the rock cycle. Use the following words to fill the empty places.

sedimentary rocks   igneous rocks   magma

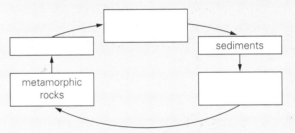

sediments

metamorphic rocks

c Sandstone is a sedimentary rock, basalt is an igneous rock. Sandstone often contains fossils, basalt does not contain fossils. Explain why.

28 The continents have moved position during the last 200 million years.

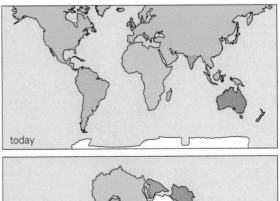

today

200 million years ago

Give two pieces of evidence which support this idea.

8.1 *Quick and slow*

A few seconds, or a few days – chemical reactions can be very quick, or very slow. This can be good news and bad!

The same change, but different speeds.

A change is taking place to both these cars. Tyres are being removed and replaced by other tyres. The change is the same in both cases, but the different conditions will make one change happen much quicker than the other one.

In some ways, a chemical reaction is similar to a tyre change. Atoms can be removed and replaced by other atoms. Altering the conditions for a chemical change (reaction) can make the change go quicker or slower.

The speed of a chemical reaction is called the **rate of reaction**.

Some chemical reactions happen very quickly – such as an explosion.

A very fast reaction!

Other reactions are not very fast. An iron nail rusts slowly. If light shines on a newspaper for some weeks, the paper slowly changes colour.

Sometimes it is helpful to *change* the speed of a chemical reaction. You may need to slow down one reaction, but speed up another.

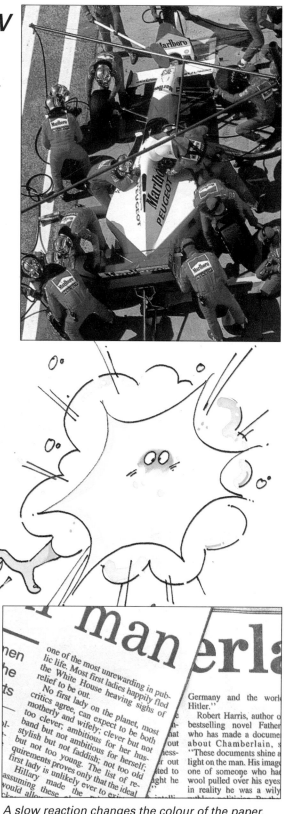

A slow reaction changes the colour of the paper.

Slow them down

Astronauts from the USA walked on the moon in 1969. They wore special spacesuits made of rubber. These are now in a museum in Washington. The museum has a problem – the rubber is reacting with air and decaying. The museum staff must slow down this reaction, so the suits don't rot away. They know that reactions go slower when they are cold, so they keep the suits in special cupboards at a low temperature of –10°C.

Speed them up

Plastic litter is a big problem, because it won't rot away very quickly (it is **non-biodegradable**). Scientists are trying to make plastics that rot quicker, so that there is less plastic litter to deal with.

Have you ever been to the dentist for a filling? A chemical reaction makes the filling harden and set. The longer it takes to set, the longer you have to wait before you can eat. This is another reaction which you want to happen quickly.

Back on Earth, this rubber suit is reacting with oxygen and rotting …

… but this plastic doesn't rot as quickly as we'd like.

QUESTIONS

1 Complete the sentences by using these words: **quick   quickly   slow   slowly.**

  a Rusting is a very _____ chemical reaction, but a burning firework is a very _____ reaction.

  b An iron fence will rust more _____ if you paint it.

  c An egg will cook more _____ in hot water than in warm water.

2 Josh and Tina are both cooking the same amount of spaghetti. Josh finishes in 10 minutes. Tina's takes 13 minutes. Which one has the faster rate of reaction?

3 Use the information on these pages to make two lists of reactions:

  a reactions you would want to speed up.

  b reactions you would want to slow down. Try to think of more examples.

KEY IDEAS

Some reactions go very quickly, and some go very slowly.

Sometimes you need to change the speed of a chemical reaction.

8.2 *Control your speed*

If you leave the lid off a tin of paint, only the top surface will set. The paint below is still liquid. Yet if the paint is spread onto a wall, it all dries and sets fairly quickly. Why?

Surface area

When paint dries, it reacts with oxygen. In the tin, only the top surface can combine with oxygen in the air. After being painted onto a wall, *all* the liquid comes into contact with oxygen, so it reacts more quickly. The paint has a greater **surface area**.

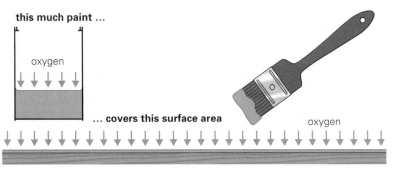

Paint dries quicker with a bigger surface area.

Skiers sometimes carry handwarmers on very cold days. These are packets of very fine *powdered* iron. When the packet is opened, the iron reacts with oxygen in the air – and this reaction gives out heat. You won't see skiers carrying *lumps* of iron, though. They know that powdered iron has a greater surface area than a lump of iron, so it can react more quickly with the oxygen.

Temperature

Mrs Edwards runs a fish and chip shop. She changes uncooked potatoes into chips by heating them in very hot oil. This is a chemical reaction. What would happen if Mrs Edwards turned down the temperature of the oil slightly? There would probably be a bigger queue, as the chips would take longer to cook! So to speed up cooking, increase the temperature.

All chemical reactions go quicker when they are hotter.

Lower temperatures mean longer to wait.

Concentration

Imagine two glasses filled with the same amount of water. You put a little orange squash in the first glass, and a lot of orange squash in the second. The orange colour is darker in the second glass – the drink is said to be more concentrated.

The people in the photo are injured. They sit inside a tank which is filled with oxygen under pressure for a few hours each day.

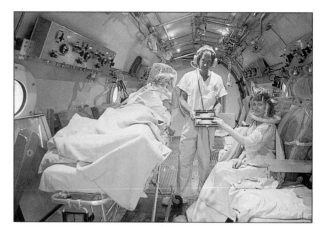

A bigger oxygen concentration will heal an injury quicker.

Our bodies need oxygen to mend damaged muscles. The air around us contains oxygen, but only about 20% of the air is oxygen. In the tank, there is 100% oxygen. So when the people breathe inside the tank, the lungs get more oxygen per breath than from normal air. The tank has a bigger **concentration** of oxygen than normal air – and so the muscles heal quicker.

Chemical reactions go quicker if you increase the concentration of substances.

Bigger concentrations make faster reactions.

QUESTIONS

1 Finish these sentences:

   a Twigs will catch fire quicker than logs because …

   b Food goes off more slowly in a fridge than in a room because …

   c Adding water to an acid makes it react more slowly because …

2 Nizam paints his bedroom wall. He then turns his radiator on. Will this make the paint set quicker or slower?

3 To make a barbecue heat up as quickly as possible, what size charcoal pieces should you use – large or small? Try to explain why.

KEY IDEAS

Chemical reactions can be speeded up by:

– increasing the temperature

– increasing the surface area (using smaller size bits)

– increasing the concentration of a substance.

8.3 *It's all about collisions*

Imagine you're in a dodgem car at a funfair.
What can you do to make sure you hit the other cars
more often? And how is that like a chemical reaction?

Chemical reactions can only happen when particles of different substances collide. To speed up reactions, you have to make the particles collide more often. How?

Particles in a container are like cars at a funfair. Each dodgem collision makes a bit of reaction. For a faster reaction you need more collisions per minute.

Particles are like dodgems – they move and collide.

Changing the temperature

One way to make more collisions is to make the dodgems move faster. If they all move faster, they will collide more often. (If they all move very slowly, they will have fewer collisions.)

If you increase the temperature, you make particles move quicker. This makes them collide more often, so reactions happen more quickly.

Faster movement means more collisions.

Changing the concentration

Back to the dodgems – is there another way to make more collisions? You can put more dodgems into the same space. This makes the dodgems closer together, so again there are more collisions.

Packing closer together makes more collisions.

The word *concentration* means the number of particles in a certain space. For example, you can talk about the concentration of an acid solution – you mean the number of acid particles dissolved in a certain amount of water. If you increase the concentration of a substance, its particles are more 'packed together'. So they collide more often, and the reaction goes faster.

Changing the surface area

Solids which are broken into little pieces have a bigger surface. So moving particles of liquids or gases can collide with the solid surface more often. This makes the reaction go faster.

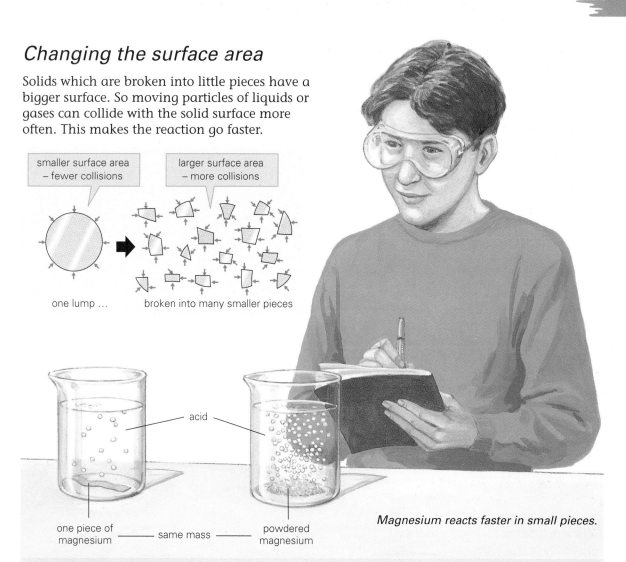

smaller surface area – fewer collisions

larger surface area – more collisions

one lump …   broken into many smaller pieces

acid

one piece of magnesium —— same mass —— powdered magnesium

Magnesium reacts faster in small pieces.

QUESTIONS

1 Complete these sentences:

a When a liquid is heated, the particles move _____. The rate of reaction is _____.

b Liquids react more slowly when they are cold, because the particles don't _____ so often.

c A high concentration means more _____ are crowded together.

2 Rory has two bowls of soup – one is very hot, and the other is very cold. In your own words, describe the differences between the particles in the two bowls.

3 A small piece of magnesium is put into a beaker of acid. It takes 6 minutes to finish reacting. If the concentration of the acid was doubled, how long would a similar piece of magnesium take to finish reacting?

KEY IDEAS

Heat makes particles move faster, and collide more often.

Higher concentrations mean particles are closer together, so they collide more often.

Smaller pieces react faster because they have a bigger surface area.

8.4 *Investigating rates of reaction*

***How fast can you do your homework?
How slowly does the traffic move in
the rush-hour? How can you find out?***

Finding out these answers is like investigating
the rate of a chemical reaction. So what do
you have to measure?

In a downhill ski race, the skiers do not race
all together. Each skis on his or her own, and
the time to reach the finish is measured. The
distance skied is the same for everybody, so the
fastest skier is the one with the shortest time.

You use a similar idea to compare the speeds
of chemical reactions.

Timing tells you who was quickest.

A photographer uses a 'fixer' to develop photos. It contains a
chemical called sodium thiosulphate. After using the fixer, the
photographer recycles the solution – it contains sulphur, which can be
used again. To get the sulphur back, the photographer adds an acid to
the used fixer. After a while, sulphur appears as a yellow solid. The
sulphur makes it harder and harder to see through the liquid.

Suki is a photographer. She wants to recycle the sulphur from her
fixer as quickly as possible. She thinks that increasing the
temperature will help. She set up this experiment to test her idea.

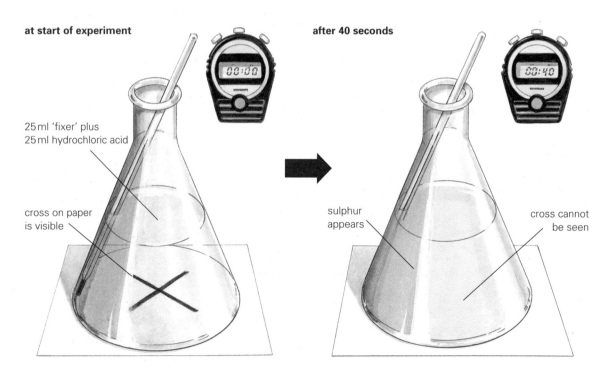

at start of experiment   **after 40 seconds**

25 ml 'fixer' plus
25 ml hydrochloric acid

cross on paper
is visible

sulphur
appears

cross cannot
be seen

Suki set up her experiment like this.

She did the same experiment at five different temperatures. To make it a fair test, she kept everything else the same during each experiment. She timed how long it took for the cross to disappear in each experiment.

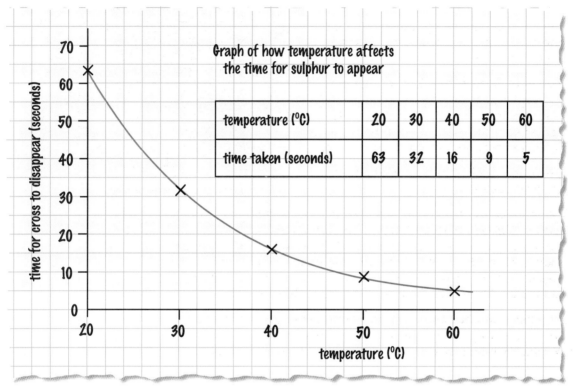

Graph of how temperature affects the time for sulphur to appear

temperature (°C)	20	30	40	50	60
time taken (seconds)	63	32	16	9	5

Here are the results Suki wrote down, and the graph she drew.

Suki drew a smooth curve through the points on her graph. The graph makes it easier to see a pattern in her results. It shows that increasing the temperature *did* make the reaction go faster. The cross disappeared fastest when the liquid was hottest. The experiment proved that her idea (her prediction) was correct.

QUESTIONS

1 Look at the diagram of Suki's experiment.
   Suggest three things she did to make it a fair test.

2 Suki did the experiment *once* at each temperature.
   What could she do to check her results are reliable?

3 Draw a labelled diagram to show how Suki could separate the solid sulphur from the liquids in the flask.

4 Each bit of sulphur was made when an acid particle and a 'fixer' particle collided. Why was sulphur made quicker as the mixture of acid and fixer got hotter? (Use the words 'particle' and 'collide' in your answer.)

KEY IDEAS

You can do experiments to compare the speed of reactions.

To investigate the speed of a reaction, you must measure the time for a substance to disappear, or for a new substance to be made.

8.5 *Catalysts*

A portable hairstyler uses an expensive metal to make beautiful curls. How?

Hairstylers need to get hot to do their job. Heat is produced when butane fuel reacts with oxygen (in a combustion reaction). The centre of the styler has a tube made of an expensive metal, platinum. The platinum helps the butane and oxygen react faster – but the platinum is *not* used up. The platinum is a **catalyst** in this reaction.

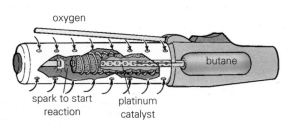

A platinum catalyst speeds up the reaction inside a portable hairstyler.

Catalysts are very useful, because they speed up chemical reactions. There are three important things about all catalysts.

- They are not used up during the reaction.

- Only small amounts of catalyst are needed.

- Different catalysts speed up different reactions.

Catalysts are used in many industrial reactions. For example, sulphuric acid is made in chemical factories by the Contact Process. Without heat, the reaction is very slow. But heat costs money. Adding a catalyst makes the reaction cheaper, because less heat is needed to make the reaction go quickly. Lower temperatures also make the reaction safer.

How do catalysts work?

Imagine you had to cycle over a very large hill. It would be quicker if there was a tunnel through the hill. Catalysts work like that – they help the reaction get from start to finish, using a shorter route.

Catalysts provide a short cut, so reactions finish more quickly.

Enzymes

Bread contains a substance called starch. When you eat bread, your body has to change the starch into sugar. This is a slow reaction. So your body makes its own catalyst, to speed up the change. The catalyst is called amylase, and is in your saliva. Amylase is an example of an **enzyme**. Enzymes are catalysts which speed up reactions in living things.

Enzymes are made inside animals and plants. You can make use of these enzymes in many ways. For example, many people like to eat gammon with fresh pineapple on top. This idea began because fresh pineapple contains enzymes, which help to break down the gammon – making it easier to chew.

Although they are made in living things, enzymes are *not* alive. Each enzyme is a chemical substance which:

- is made of protein

- speeds up just one particular reaction

- works best at one particular temperature

- is destroyed by being too hot or too cold.

Enzymes in the pineapple can make the meat softer.

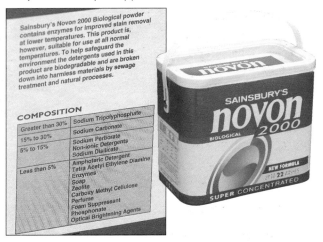

Biological washing powders contain enzymes to help break down dirt and stains.

QUESTIONS

1 Complete this sentence:
Catalysts make reactions go _____ but are not _____ up during the reaction.

2 Platinum is a very expensive metal.

a Explain why it is used in the hairstyler.

b Suggest why it doesn't make the hairstyler too expensive.

3 Hydrogen peroxide is a chemical that slowly gives off oxygen gas. If a piece of potato is added, oxygen gas appears much faster.

a A potato is part of a living thing. Why can a potato make the reaction go faster?

b 2g of potato is added to hydrogen peroxide at the start of the reaction. How much potato will be there at the end of the reaction?

KEY IDEAS

Catalysts speed up chemical reactions, but aren't used up in the reaction.

Enzymes are catalysts made in living things. They only work at certain temperatures.

Each catalyst or enzyme speeds up a different reaction.

8.6 *Bakers and brewers*

What do a loaf of bread, a glass of wine and a pint of beer have in common?

These people make beer, wine and bread. They all use the same chemical reaction. It is known as **fermentation**.

sugar → carbon dioxide + alcohol

This reaction needs enzymes to make it go fast enough. So a living thing called **yeast** is added. Yeast makes enzymes which speed up this process.

Beer

To brew beer, grain from barley is mixed with warm water and hops. This makes a sugary liquid. Yeast is added, and fermentation begins. The sugar changes into carbon dioxide gas and alcohol. (You must let the gas escape, or the container could explode!)

The temperature must be kept exactly right during fermentation. Too hot or too cold, and the enzymes won't work.

The alcohol that is made kills the yeast. So the reaction stops when all the yeast has been killed.

Wine

Wine is made in much the same way as beer. Usually grapes are used, instead of barley, to provide the sugar for the reaction.

There are lots of different beers and wines on sale these days – what's the difference? The alcohol is the same chemical in all of them. The different flavours come from different types of grapes, barley, water or other ingredients.

So many beers – all made by fermentation.

Bread

To make bread, mix flour, water, sugar and yeast into a dough. Leave it in a warm place, and the dough will get bigger. Again fermentation is changing the sugar into alcohol and carbon dioxide. Bubbles of this gas makes the dough 'rise'. When you bake it in a hot oven, the alcohol evaporates away.

Fermentation made the bread rise.

Some enzymes made the bread – other enzymes will break it down.

Yoghurt-making

Baking and brewing use enzymes from yeast. A different enzyme is used to make yoghurt. When you add it to milk, the enzyme changes sugar in the milk into lactic acid. This makes the milk go thick and more sour. You have changed the milk into yoghurt.

Yoghurt is made using enzymes, but not from yeast.

QUESTIONS

1 Complete these sentences:
   a During fermentation, enzymes from _____ help to change _____ into alcohol and _____ _____ gas.
   b This reaction is used to make beer, _____ and _____.

2 When bread dough rises, alcohol is made. Why can't we taste it in the bread?

3 Pitta bread is a very flat type of bread. It is made in a similar way to other bread, but no yeast is added. Why doesn't it rise like other bread?

4 Beer, wine, bread and yoghurt are all made using enzymes. Which one is the odd one out? Explain your answer.

KEY IDEAS

Bread, beer and wine are made by fermentation.

Fermentation uses enzymes from yeast.

$$sugar \xrightarrow{yeast} alcohol + carbon\ dioxide$$

Another enzyme is used to change milk into yoghurt.

8.7 *Things are hotting up*

Cooking with chemicals can come in handy, when you're a long way from a kitchen!

Having lunch is never easy for soldiers in battle. They often don't have time to eat, and may not find anything tasty nearby! This soldier is luckier than most. Although he's a long way from a kitchen, he knows that he will have a hot meal. He is carrying an MRE – a 'Meal, Ready-to-Eat'. This will give him a hot lunch, thanks to a chemical reaction.

The food is in a small packet. The soldier puts this into a special pouch – known as a 'flameless heater'. It contains magnesium, a metal. He adds water to the pouch. The magnesium reacts with the water and produces heat. The temperature inside the pouch goes up, and the food becomes hot.

During the reaction, chemical energy was changed into heat energy.

chemical energy $\longrightarrow$ heat energy

There are many other reactions which change chemical energy into heat energy.

This soldier uses a chemical reaction to get a quick, hot meal.

- When you use a Bunsen burner in a laboratory, the gas (methane) reacts with oxygen, and gives out heat.

- Some factories get rid of old car tyres by burning them. This reaction releases (gives out) heat. (The heat boils water, and the steam is then used to generate electricity.)

- When an acid reacts with an alkali (a neutralisation reaction), the temperature goes up. Heat energy is released.

In all these reactions, stored chemical energy changes into heat energy. These reactions are called **exothermic** reactions.

Magnesium reacts with water, producing heat for the food.

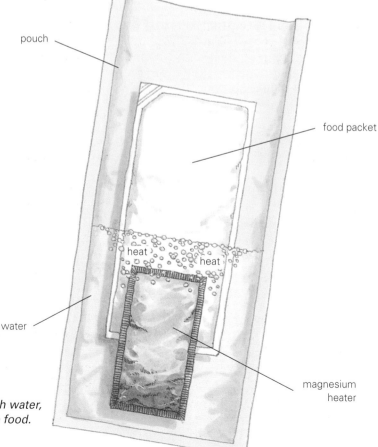

pouch

food packet

heat   heat

water

magnesium heater

Some other reactions won't happen unless they are given heat. If you shape a piece of clay and put it into a cold oven, nothing happens. But when the oven is heated, the clay changes into a piece of pottery. This change needs heat.

If you dissolve potassium chloride crystals in water, the water gets colder. Heat from the water has been used to help the solid potassium chloride dissolve.

Reactions which need heat energy are called **endothermic** reactions.

To remember these two words, think of *exit* and *entrance*:

■ *ex*othermic – heat goes out (*exits*)

■ *en*dothermic – heat goes in (*enters*).

Fuels

A fuel is a chemical which burns in oxygen and gives out heat. Coal, charcoal, camping gas, petrol, wood – they are all fuels. Burning a fuel is an exothermic reaction.

Many different fuels burn, but the reaction is always exothermic – they give out heat.

Heat energy is given to the clay – this is an endothermic reaction.

QUESTIONS

1 Complete this paragraph, using these words:
   up exothermic water magnesium heat
   To heat an MRE, a soldier adds _____ to the pouch. This reacts with a metal called _____, and _____ is given out. This makes the temperature of the food go _____ . This type of reaction is called an _____ reaction.

2 For each of these reactions, decide if they are **exothermic** or **endothermic**.
   a cooking popcorn
   b burning petrol in a car engine
   c mixing sulphuric acid with an alkali.

3 You are given twigs of three different woods – ash, beech and pine. Write a plan for an investigation to find out which wood gives out most heat when burned.

KEY IDEAS

Some reactions give out heat – they are called exothermic reactions.

Some reactions use up heat – they are called endothermic reactions.

Fuels burn and give out heat – combustion is an exothermic reaction.

8.8 *Current chemistry*

Do you need an alarm clock to get you started in the mornings? Some chemical reactions need heat energy to get started. Others need electrical energy to make them happen.

You can pass electricity through a liquid using the equipment shown in the diagram. The two conducting rods dipping into the water are the electrodes. They have opposite electrical charges: positive (+) and negative (−).

Splitting compounds

The liquid is a compound. It conducts electricity because it contains charged particles, called **ions**. In a liquid, these particles (ions) can move around. Opposite electrical charges always attract each other. So ions with a positive (+) charge move to the electrode with a negative (−) charge. Ions with a negative (−) charge move towards the electrode with a positive (+) charge. This process is known as **electrolysis**.

Solid compounds don't conduct electricity, because the particles can't move. They have to be melted or dissolved in water. Then the ions *can* move to the electrodes.

As the ions move in opposite directions, the compound splits into two bits. If the liquid is copper chloride, copper goes one way and chlorine goes the other.

Electrolysis uses electricity to split a compound into its elements.

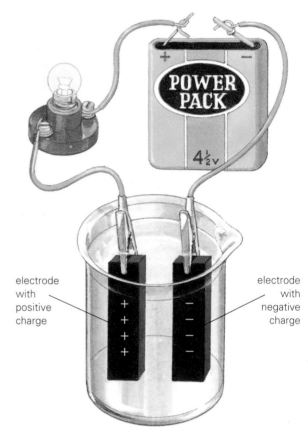

electrode with positive charge

electrode with negative charge

The liquid conducts and completes the electrical circuit.

solid – not conducting

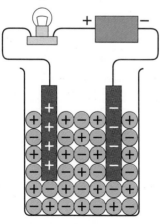

liquid – conducting

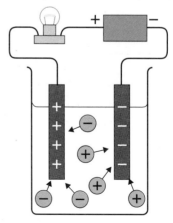

Ions can't move in a solid, but can move in a liquid.

154

Which ions go where?

- Metal (and hydrogen) ions are + ... and go to the – electrode.

- Non-metal ions are – ... and go to the + electrode.

You could try to remember it as:

- **MAP** (**M**etals **A**re **P**ositive)

- **NAN** (**N**on-metals **A**re **N**egative)

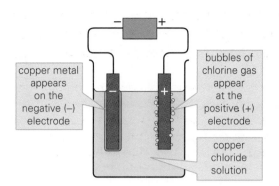

Copper and chlorine come from copper chloride.

Splitting water

Water can conduct electricity. Water's formula is H_2O – it contains hydrogen and oxygen. During electrolysis:

- hydrogen gas is collected at the negative (–) electrode

- oxygen gas is collected at the positive (+) electrode

So electricity can split water into hydrogen and oxygen.

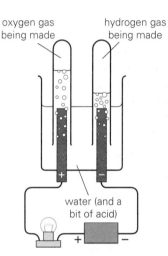

Water can be split into its elements by electrolysis.

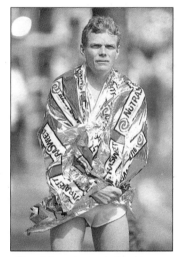

Aluminium is made by the electrolysis of aluminium oxide.

QUESTIONS

1 Complete the passage, using these words.
   liquid   ions   electricity   electrode

   Electrolysis is a reaction where _____ is passed through a _____. Charged particles, called _____, are attracted to an _____ with an opposite charge.

2 If these substances were made during electrolysis, would they go to the positive (+) or negative (–) electrode?

   a copper

   b oxygen

   c aluminium

   d chlorine.

3 Solid copper chloride is a compound which is made of ions. Why doesn't it conduct electricity?

KEY IDEAS

Electricity can split some liquid compounds into elements. This is called electrolysis.

Metals (and hydrogen) go to negative (–) electrodes.

Non-metal gases go to positive (+) electrodes.

8.9 *Splitting salt and coating copper*

How can electricity help change salt into soap, and cheap jewellery into shiny silver?

Useful things from salt

Salt is a raw material. It is found dissolved in sea water, and as a rock underground. Salt is a compound called sodium chloride (NaCl). Some salt is used for cooking, and some is put on roads in winter to melt the ice. But a lot of salt is used to make other useful substances.

Rock salt is mined from rocks underground.

Salt is changed by passing electricity through brine – a solution of salt dissolved in water. During this reaction, ions from sodium chloride (the salt) *and* from the water (H_2O) are attracted to the electrodes. The result is:

- hydrogen gas (H_2) appears at the negative (–) electrode

- chlorine gas (Cl_2) appears at the positive (+) electrode

- sodium hydroxide solution (NaOH) is left behind.

All three of these substances are useful and can be sold. You can see some of the uses in the diagram.

You could test all three substances in a laboratory.

- hydrogen gas 'pops' with a lighted splint

- chlorine gas bleaches the colour from damp litmus paper

- sodium hydroxide solution is an alkali, so turns red litmus blue.

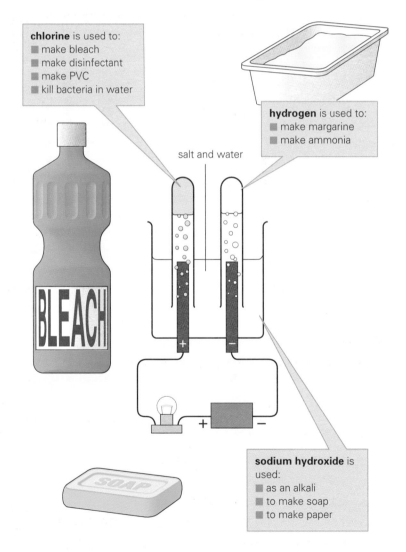

chlorine is used to:
- make bleach
- make disinfectant
- make PVC
- kill bacteria in water

hydrogen is used to:
- make margarine
- make ammonia

salt and water

sodium hydroxide is used:
- as an alkali
- to make soap
- to make paper

Salt helps to make many other useful substances.

Coating with metal

You can buy silver-plated jewellery, chromium-plated taps, and tin-plated cans. These objects have one metal as a thin coating on another metal. Electrolysis is used to do this.

During electrolysis, metals often appear on the negative (−) electrode. They go there because metal ions always have a positive (+) charge, so are attracted to the negative (−) electrode.

To coat an object with a metal, use the object as the negative (−) electrode. The liquid must contain a compound with the coating metal in it (such as silver nitrate solution for silver-plating). When electricity flows, the metal ions (+) will move and stick onto the negative (−) electrode.

This process is called **electroplating**. The metal coating protects the object from corrosion by air and water.

This technique can also be used to move copper from one electrode to the other — purifying it in the process.

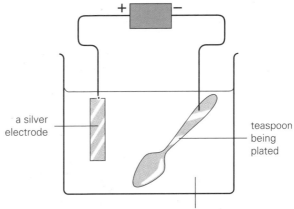

a silver electrode

teaspoon being plated

compound containing silver ions (e.g. silver nitrate)

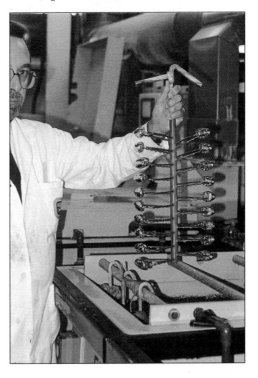

Electrolysis is used to silver-plate teaspoons.

QUESTIONS

1 Salt is a compound. What is its chemical name and formula?

2 Salt is a raw material, found underground and in sea water. Explain how you could get solid salt from each place.

3 Name the three substance produced by the electrolysis of salt. Give two uses of each one.

4 An iron dustbin is electroplated with a zinc coating.
   a Draw a labelled diagram to show how zinc is added.
   b What is the benefit of adding the zinc?

9.1 *Mind your language*

If you saw 'H₂O' in a foreign language newspaper, would you know what it meant? If you recognised that the newspaper was writing about water, you would be using chemistry's international language – symbols.

étain/silice (Sn/RU atomique = 0.1) et rhodium/charbon actif.

$$RCO_2CH_3 + H_2 \longrightarrow RCOOH + CH_4$$

En outre, les réactions d'hydrogénolyse sont généralement favorisées par la présence de grosses particules métalliques.

You might not speak the language, but the symbols tell you it's about chemistry.

Elements

There are about 108 different elements in the world, and each one has its own symbol. The symbol is one or two letters (the first letter is always a capital letter).

Some common chemical symbols					
sulphur	S	hydrogen	H	oxygen	O
aluminium	Al	zinc	Zn	helium	He
iron	Fe	gold	Au	sodium	Na
copper	Cu	carbon	C	chlorine	Cl

You can see *all* the symbols on a periodic table.

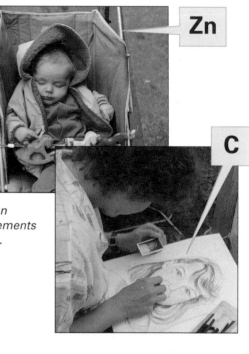

Symbols can describe elements around you.

Watch the gases

Helium gas contains helium atoms. Helium is a noble gas, so the atoms don't join with any others. You write it as He.

Chlorine gas contains chlorine atoms. But in chlorine, pairs of atoms join together to make molecules. To show that the atoms are in pairs you write Cl₂, not just Cl. You do this with most non-metal gases (except the noble gases).

Some common gas molecules			
chlorine	Cl₂	oxygen	O₂
nitrogen	N₂	hydrogen	H₂

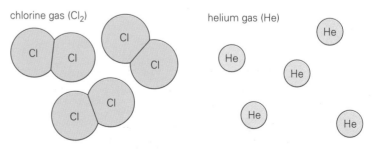

chlorine gas (Cl₂)

helium gas (He)

Chlorine gas is Cl₂, helium gas is He.

Some common compounds	
acids	
hydrochloric acid	HCl
sulphuric acid	H_2SO_4
alkali	
sodium hydroxide	NaOH
gases	
carbon dioxide	CO_2
sulphur dioxide	SO_2
carbon monoxide	CO
ammonia	NH_3
methane (natural gas)	CH_4
solids	
sodium chloride (salt)	NaCl
calcium carbonate (limestone)	$CaCO_3$
copper sulphate	$CuSO_4$

Some common compounds and their formulas.

Compounds

Most substances around you are compounds: they contain different elements joined together. For example, water is a compound. It is made of hydrogen (H) and oxygen (O) joined together. This is shown by using the symbols to write water's formula: H_2O. (The 2 shows that there are two hydrogen atoms for every one oxygen atom.)

A chemical formula lists different symbols and numbers. It shows you which elements are in a compound, and how many of each atom. The table shows the formulas of some compounds you may know.

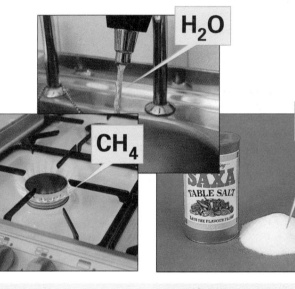

QUESTIONS

1   Match each element with its correct symbol.

   sulphur   gold   aluminium   carbon   helium

   Al   Au   He   S   C

2   Write down the formula of each of these compounds:
   a sodium chloride
   b water
   c carbon monoxide
   d hydrochloric acid
   e ammonia.

3   Coal often contains tiny amounts of sulphur. When this sulphur is burned, it forms sulphur dioxide. This is shown in a word equation:

   sulphur + oxygen → sulphur dioxide

   Write a symbol equation for this reaction.

KEY IDEAS

Each element has its own symbol.

The formula of a compound shows the different elements in it.

9.2 *Too small to count*

It's hard enough counting grains of sand, or weighing smoke. But atoms are too tiny to be seen or weighed. So how can you measure them?

Have you ever bought sweets from a pic'n'mix counter? When you've made your choice, the shop assistant won't count the sweets – she'll weigh the sweets. This is because different sweets have a different weight, or mass. In 100 g you might get 4 gobstoppers but 20 winegums, for example. You could have lots of small sweets, or a few bigger ones.

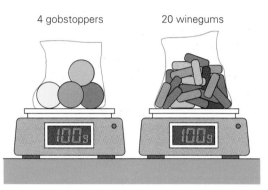

4 gobstoppers   20 winegums

Atoms are like sweets – each type has a different mass.

Measuring atoms

Atoms are also measured using their mass. The problem is that one atom is too small to be weighed. For example, one hydrogen atom has a mass of 0.000 000 000 000 000 000 000 000 17 g. This wouldn't show up on normal scales. And even if it did, it's not an easy number to use – you might easily miss out a '0'!

So chemists have an easier way to compare atoms. Hydrogen is the smallest, lightest atom – and is given a value of 1. A carbon atom is 12 times heavier than a hydrogen atom, so it has a value of 12. A sodium atom is 23 times heavier then a hydrogen atom, so it has a value of 23.

It's like comparing sweets. Imagine the 'lightest' sweet in a shop is a wine gum. So give it a value of 1. If a gobstopper is 5 times heavier than a wine gum, then the gobstopper has a value of 5.

A value has been worked out for every element. It is called the **relative atomic mass**. It can be written as A_r. The table shows you lots of A_r values.

This scale makes things easier for you. For example, gold has a relative atomic mass of 197. So if you had 100 million gold atoms, you know that they would be 197 times heavier than 100 million hydrogen atoms.

A sodium atom has a relative mass of 23.

Relative atomic masses (A_r) of some elements			
calcium (Ca)	40	iron (Fe)	56
carbon (C)	12	lead (Pb)	207
copper (Cu)	64	nitrogen (N)	14
helium (He)	4	oxygen (O)	16
hydrogen (H)	1	sodium (Na)	23

How heavy are compounds?

The formula of a compound tells you which type of atoms it contains. For example, methane's formula is CH_4. Methane is made of molecules. Each molecule contains 1 carbon atom and 4 hydrogen atoms. If you add together the right number of relative atomic masses, you can work out the **relative formula mass** (sometimes called relative molecular mass) of the compound:

- $C = 12$

- $H = 1$

- So $CH_4 = 12+1+1+1+1 = 16$.

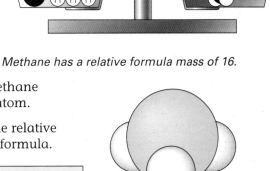

1 carbon
+
4 hydrogen atoms

1 methane molecule (CH_4)

Methane has a relative formula mass of 16.

The relative formula mass of methane is 16. A methane molecule is 16 times heavier than one hydrogen atom.

You can use relative atomic masses to work out the relative formula mass of any compound – *if* you know its formula.

An example

What is the relative formula mass of ammonia, NH_3?
Relative atomic mass (A_r) values: nitrogen (N) = 14
hydrogen (H) = 1
A molecule of NH_3 contains 1 nitrogen atom and 3 hydrogen atoms.
So the relative formula mass = $14+1+1+1 = $ **17**.

A molecule of ammonia has the formula NH_3.

QUESTIONS

1 Use the table of relative atomic masses to match each element with its value:

   carbon   iron   oxygen   lead   hydrogen   nitrogen
   56   1   12   207   14   16

2 Copper has a relative atomic mass of 64.
   How many hydrogen atoms would weigh the same as 1 atom of copper?

3 Work out the relative formula mass of these compounds, using the relative atomic masses listed below:

   a carbon dioxide, CO_2

   b lime, CaO

   c water, H_2O

   d limestone, $CaCO_3$

   A_r values: C = 12, O = 16, H = 1, Ca = 40.

KEY IDEAS

Relative atomic masses (known as A_r values) show how heavy each element is. The lightest atom, hydrogen, has an A_r value of 1.

The mass of compounds can be compared using relative formula mass.

Add together relative atomic masses to calculate a relative formula mass.

9.3 *How much is useful?*

If you find an ore like copper oxide, how much of it will be copper? Chemists need to know, to decide if it's worth mining it.

Copper ore is often known as malachite. It's a rock found in the ground. It contains the compound copper oxide. The formula is CuO.

The relative atomic masses (A_r) are:

■ copper (Cu) = 64

■ oxygen (O) = 16

The relative formula mass of CuO is 64 + 16 = 80.

So if you found 80g of copper oxide, 64g would be copper and 16g would be oxygen.

If you found 80 tonnes of copper oxide, 64 tonnes would be copper and 16 tonnes would be oxygen.

The ore contains copper … but how much?

What percentage?

It is often helpful to know the percentage of a compound that is useful.

It's not worth digging a hole like this if there isn't much metal in the rocks.

> The percentage (%) of element in a compound is:
>
> $\dfrac{\text{mass of element}}{\text{mass of compound}} \times 100$

In the case of copper oxide:

$\dfrac{\text{mass of copper}}{\text{mass of copper oxide}} \times 100$

In this example, the percentage of copper in copper oxide is:

$\dfrac{64}{80} \times 100 = 80\%$

Fertilisers

Farmers and gardeners buy fertilisers to add to the soil. These can provide three elements which plants need – nitrogen (N), phosphorus (P) and potassium (K). Fertilisers are compounds containing one or more of these elements. But what percentage of each compound is useful for the plants?

Look at these examples. Fertilisers A and B both provide nitrogen – but which one provides most nitrogen?

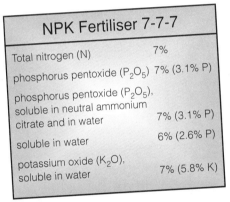

NPK Fertiliser 7-7-7

Total nitrogen (N)	7%
phosphorus pentoxide (P_2O_5)	7% (3.1% P)
phosphorus pentoxide (P_2O_5), soluble in neutral ammonium citrate and in water	7% (3.1% P)
soluble in water	6% (2.6% P)
potassium oxide (K_2O), soluble in water	7% (5.8% K)

The percentage of N, P or K tells you how much of the fertiliser is useful.

Fertiliser A – ammonium chloride (NH_4Cl)

Relative atomic mass of elements: N = 14
H = 1
Cl = 35.5

Formula: N H$_4$ Cl

Relative formula mass = 14+1+1+1+1+35.5 = 53.5

So 53.5g of the compound contains 14g of nitrogen (N).

So the percentage of N = $\frac{14}{53.5} \times 100$ = **26.17%**

Fertiliser B – ammonium nitrate (NH_4NO_3)

Relative atomic mass of elements: N = 14
H = 1
O = 16

Formula: N H$_4$ N O$_3$

Relative formula mass = 14 + 1+1+1+1+14+16+16+16 = 80

So 80g of the compound contains 28g of nitrogen (N).

(Notice that you have to count 14 twice, because N is in the formula twice.)

So the percentage of N = $\frac{(14+14)}{80} \times 100$ = **35%**

These calculations show that fertiliser B provides more nitrogen for the plants than fertiliser A.

QUESTIONS

1 Complete this sentence:
   In any sample of copper oxide, _____% of the mass is copper, and _____% of the mass is _____.

2 Many toothpastes contain sodium fluoride, NaF. What percentage of the mass of this compound is fluorine?
   A_r values: Na = 23, F = 19.

3 Aluminium and lead are both found in ores. Calculate the percentage of:
   a lead in lead oxide, PbO_2
   b aluminium in aluminium oxide, Al_2O_3
   A_r values: lead (Pb) = 207, oxygen (O) = 16, aluminium (Al) = 27

9.4 *The Reedroc ten*

There are so many reactions, and they all seem so different. How can you make them easier to remember?

Millions of chemical reactions affect your life every day. Nobody could remember all of these reactions. But many reactions are similar – they have the same features. Chemists give names to some of these features.

Consider this reaction, known as the thermit reaction:

aluminium + iron oxide → aluminium oxide + iron

This reaction could be described in four different ways:

- displacement – aluminium replaces iron

- oxidation – aluminium joins with oxygen

- reduction – iron loses oxygen

- exothermic – as heat is given out.

You probably know 10 useful ways of describing reactions. You could call them the
REEDROC TEN – can you see why?

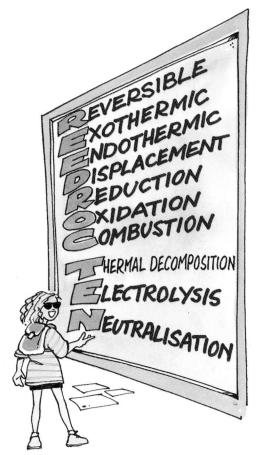

The **REEDROC TEN** *helps you remember different reactions.*

Reactions can be …

Reversible
Some products can turn back to how they started. For example:

$$\text{white copper sulphate} \underset{\text{DRY}}{\overset{\text{WET}}{\rightleftharpoons}} \text{blue copper sulphate}$$

Exothermic
Some reactions give out heat (e.g. burning wood).

Endothermic
Other reactions need to be given heat (e.g. frying an egg).

Displacement
A reactive element replaces a less reactive element in a compound. For example:

magnesium + copper oxide → magnesium oxide + copper

Reduction
Loss of oxygen is called reduction (e.g. iron oxide is reduced to iron in a blast furnace).

The raw eggs need heat to change into cooked eggs – an endothermic reaction.

Oxidation

In some reactions a substance combines with oxygen
(e.g. iron is oxidised when it rusts, food is oxidised during respiration).

Combustion

A fuel burns and reacts with oxygen (e.g. when coal burns):

carbon + oxygen → carbon dioxide

Thermal decomposition

Heating some compounds makes them break
into smaller bits. For example, cracking makes
oil fractions smaller and more useful; lime is
made by heating limestone.

Electrolysis

Passing electricity through liquids can split
compounds into elements. For example,
aluminium ore (aluminium oxide) splits into
aluminium and oxygen.

Neutralisation

Acids and alkalis cancel each other out, making
neutral substances.

Adding alkali neutralises acidic water.

So this list gives you 10 different ways to describe reactions.
Remember the **REEDROC TEN**!

QUESTIONS

1   For each description, decide which type of reaction it is:

a mixing two liquids changes the colour of universal indicator

b two substances react and get hotter

c passing electricity through a liquid

d a reaction which seems to go back to where it started.

2   Camping stoves burn propane gas.
Propane is a hydrocarbon, and burns like this:

propane + oxygen → carbon dioxide + water

This reaction can be called *oxidation*, *combustion* and
exothermic. Explain why it belongs in each of these groups.

3   This reaction gives off a lot of heat:

magnesium + copper oxide → magnesium oxide + copper

Explain four different names you could give to this reaction.

KEY IDEAS

Many chemical
reactions are
similar, and can be
grouped together.

SECTION C: QUESTIONS

1 Complete these sentences:

a Reactions in your body are speeded up by substances called _____.

b Reactions which give out heat are called _____.

c Using electricity to split compounds is called _____.

d Sodium chloride is the chemical name for _____.

e Hydrogen has a relative atomic mass of _____.

f The symbol ⇌ shows that a chemical reaction is _____.

g A gas used to make bleaches and disinfectants is _____.

h Particles with a charge are called _____.

i The reaction involved in making bread and beer is called _____.

j Substances which burn and give out heat are called _____.

2 A chemical reaction makes a glue set. The table shows the time taken for two different glues to set at different temperatures.

Temperature (°C)	Time to set (hours)	
	Superset	**Stickeasy**
5	72	57
10	24	41
23	8	24
40	2	6
60	1.5	3
80	0.25	1
100	0.16	0.3

a Room temperature is usually between 20 and 25°C. Which glue would set quickest at room temperature?

b What effect does changing the temperature have on the time taken for glue to set?

c Use your ideas about particles to explain why many reactions go quicker if the temperature is increased.

3 Hydrogen peroxide is a compound which slowly decomposes, giving off oxygen gas.

a How would you test a gas to prove it was oxygen?

b The other product of the reaction has the formula H_2O. What is its common name?

If you add a small amount of a solid called manganese dioxide, the reaction goes much quicker.

c What name is given to chemicals like manganese dioxide which speed up other reactions?

d At the end of the reaction, what would have happened to the mass of manganese dioxide added? Write down one suggestion:

    got bigger
    stayed the same
    got smaller

e If the manganese dioxide is added as a powder, it makes the reaction go quicker than when it is added as one lump. Why?

4 Alcohol is made from glucose (a sugar) during fermentation. A student used this experiment to investigate a fermentation reaction:

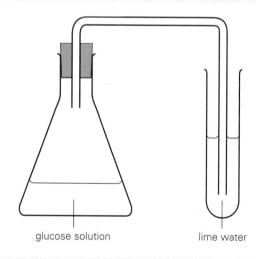

glucose solution   lime water

a What must be added to the glucose solution for fermentation to happen?

b Carbon dioxide gas is also made during the reaction. How would you know that it had been made?

5 Many washing powders are described as biological. This is because they contain enzymes, to help break down dirt and grease.

The instructions on packets of biological washing powders often say 'do not use at temperatures above 60°C'. Why?

6 Sodium chloride (salt) solution can be electrolysed using this equipment:

sodium chloride solution

The products from this reaction are very useful. Name the product formed at:

a the positive (+) electrode

b the negative (–) electrode.

c Give two uses of each of these products.

7 Which of these substances contains
i calcium **ii** nitrogen **iii** chlorine?

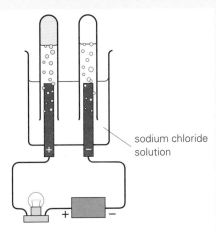

a SiO₂
b NaCl

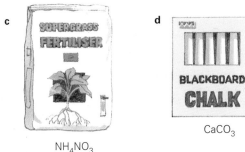

c NH₄NO₃
d CaCO₃

8 The diagrams show molecules of certain compounds. For each compound, use the diagram to help you write down its chemical formula.

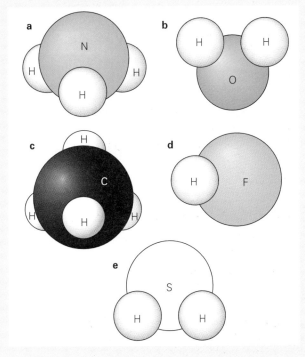

9 Ammonium nitrate is a good fertiliser. It has the formula NH_4NO_3. Ammonium nitrate is a solid, but dissolves well in water.

a Which element in ammonium nitrate makes it useful as a fertiliser?

b Apart from cost, suggest one advantage and one disadvantage of using ammonium nitrate as a fertiliser.

c Use these relative atomic masses (A_r) to work out the relative formula mass of ammonium nitrate:

A_r (N) = 14
A_r (H) = 1
A_r (O) = 16

10 Limestone, marble and chalk are all rocks which contain calcium carbonate.

a Calculate the relative formula mass of calcium carbonate, $CaCO_3$.

A_r (Ca) = 40
A_r (C) = 12
A_r (O) = 16

b Use your answer to **a** to calculate the percentage of calcium (Ca) in any sample of calcium carbonate.

Units

Units are very important in chemistry, especially when you are doing experiments and investigations.

Here are some of the measuring units you should be able to use.

Mass	Length	Volume
1000 g = 1 kg 1000 kg = 1 tonne	10 mm = 1 cm 100 cm = 1 m 1000 m = 1 km	1000 ml = 1 l 1 ml is the same as 1 cm^3 so 1000 cm^3 = 1 l
g = gram kg = kilogram	mm = millimetre cm = centimetre m = metre km = kilometre	ml = millilitre l = litre cm^3 = cubic centimetre

Time	Temperature
60 seconds = 1 minute 60 minutes = 1 hour	Use °C (degrees celsius) Remember: water freezes at 0°C water boils at 100°C

Finding an average

An investigation will be improved if you can find the average result from repeating the experiment a number of times.

To find an average:

a add up all the results
b divide by the number of results

For example

To find the average of these six numbers:
7 11 10 7 8 11

a add them up:
   7 + 11 + 10 + 7 + 8 + 11 = 54

b then divide them by 6:
   $\frac{54}{6} = 9$

The average is 9.

Working out percentages

It is sometimes useful to know the amount of one thing as a percentage of a whole amount. For example, the amount of one element in a compound, or the amount of a material used for a particular purpose.

To find a percentage:

a work out the part you are interested in
b divide this amount by the whole amount
c multiply your answer by 100

$$\frac{\text{the part you're interested in}}{\text{the whole amount}} \times 100$$

For example

A chemical factory produces 2400 tonnes of ammonia a year. 1920 tonnes are used to make fertilisers. To find the percentage of ammonia used to make fertilisers:

a the amount you are interested in is 1920

b divide this by the whole amount:

   $\frac{1920}{2400} = 0.8$

c multiply by 100:

   $0.8 \times 100 = 80\%$

Drawing a pie chart

Pie charts can be used to show how a total is made up of different parts. The whole chart represents 100%.

If you divide the chart into ten equal sections, each section represents 10%.

The data in the table shows the uses of ammonia in the UK. You can turn this into a pie chart

Step 1 Choose the biggest number – 80%.

Step 2 The number for making nylon is 5%.

Step 3 There are one and a half blank sections left, and two values to fill in – 8% and 7%.

Uses of ammonia	
making fertilisers	80%
making nitric acid	7%
making nylon	5%
other uses	8%

Eight sections are needed for 80%.

5% will be exactly half a section.

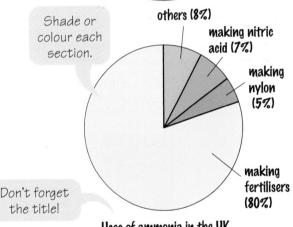

8% and 7% are very nearly the same size.

Shade or colour each section.

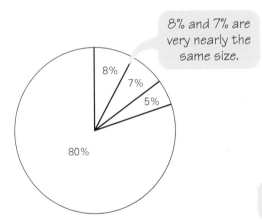

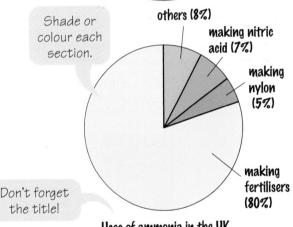

others (8%)

making nitric acid (7%)

making nylon (5%)

making fertilisers (80%)

Don't forget the title!

Uses of ammonia in the UK

Step 4 Check that you have used all the values. Label each section to show what it is. Colour the sections and give the chart a title.

Understanding pie charts

This pie chart shows the uses of copper metal.

You can see clearly that over half of all copper (58%) is used for one thing – electrical equipment. It also shows that the amounts used for plumbing/roofing and machinery are very similar (19% and 17%).

As there are lots of other uses of copper, each use has a very small percentage. To make the chart easier to understand, these small uses are added together and called 'others'.

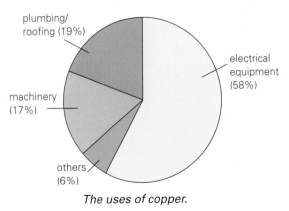

plumbing/roofing (19%)

electrical equipment (58%)

machinery (17%)

others (6%)

The uses of copper.

Drawing a bar chart

It can be useful to draw a **bar chart** to compare results or other information.

Try using this data to produce a bar chart.

Step 1 How many bars will you need? Divide the bottom of the chart into equal size spaces.

Step 2 What's the largest number needed? Choose a scale to fit the side of the chart.

Step 3 Write a label on both sides of the chart.

Step 4 Draw in each bar, check that they are at the right height.

Step 5 Give the bar chart a useful title.

Metal	Annual production (million tonnes)
aluminium	15.5
copper	8.4
lead	3.4
nickel	0.8
tin	0.2
zinc	6.8

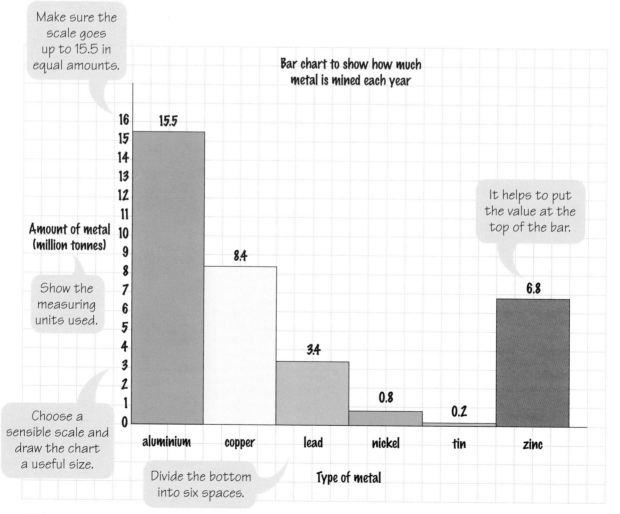

Make sure the scale goes up to 15.5 in equal amounts.

Bar chart to show how much metal is mined each year

It helps to put the value at the top of the bar.

Amount of metal (million tonnes)

Show the measuring units used.

Choose a sensible scale and draw the chart a useful size.

Divide the bottom into six spaces.

Type of metal

170

Drawing a line graph

Experiments often give you lots of numbers as results. A line graph can help you to find a pattern to these numbers.

Use this table of results and a piece of graph paper. Follow the steps to produce a line graph.

Step 1 Decide which quantity to put along the bottom of the graph. This should be the numbers that you decided *before* the experiment.

Step 2 Look at the biggest and smallest numbers needed on each side of the graph. Choose a sensible scale to fit them in.

Step 3 Write a label on each side of the graph, and show the measuring units.

Step 4 Mark each point on the graph clearly with an × (use a sharp pencil).

Time (mins)	Volume of gas (cm^3)	
	big chalk piece	chalk powder
0	0	0
$\frac{1}{2}$	23	62
1	44	130
$1\frac{1}{2}$	69	169
2	95	170
$2\frac{1}{2}$	124	170
3	152	170
$3\frac{1}{2}$	170	170
4	170	170

Step 5 Draw a smooth line through the points.

Step 6 If there is more than one line, label each line clearly.

Step 7 Give the graph a suitable title.

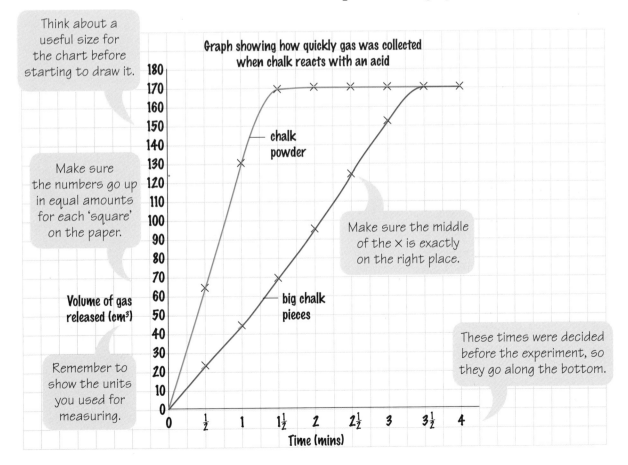

Think about a useful size for the chart before starting to draw it.

Make sure the numbers go up in equal amounts for each 'square' on the paper.

Volume of gas released (cm^3)

Remember to show the units you used for measuring.

Graph showing how quickly gas was collected when chalk reacts with an acid

chalk powder

Make sure the middle of the × is exactly on the right place.

big chalk pieces

These times were decided before the experiment, so they go along the bottom.

Time (mins)

The reactivity series of common metals

potassium

sodium

calcium

magnesium

aluminium

zinc

iron

copper

gold

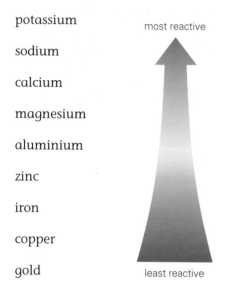

most reactive

least reactive

Atomic structure

All atoms are made up of protons, neutrons and electrons.

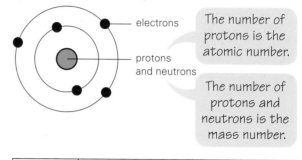

electrons

protons and neutrons

The number of protons is the atomic number.

The number of protons and neutrons is the mass number.

	Relative mass	Relative charge
proton	1	+1
neutron	1	0
electron	0 (approx)	−1

Names of chemicals

Here are a few hints to make chemical names easier to understand.

▪ Name endings

Many non-metal names end in -en or -ine.

oxygen, nitrogen
chlorine, iodine

If these non-metals are part of a compound, the ending of the name changes. Usually it becomes -ide.

sodium and chlorine become sodium chloride
iron and oxygen become iron oxide
potassium and iodine become potassium iodide
calcium and fluorine become calcium fluoride

▪ M before N

Many compounds contain a metal element joined to a non-metal.

The name of the compound always has the Metal first and the Non-metal second.

copper and oxygen make copper oxide
(not oxide copper)

Remember the alphabet: M before N (Metal before Non-metal).

▪ Spot the hydrogen

Hydrogen is in many compounds. These compounds often have unusual names.

H_2O is called water (not hydrogen oxide)
NH_3 is called ammonia (not nitrogen hydride)

Most acids contain hydrogen.

HCl is hydrochloric acid
H_2SO_4 is sulphuric acid
HNO_3 is nitric acid

The pH scale

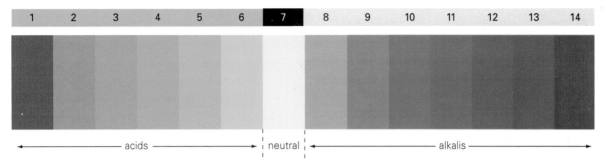

| 1 | 2 | 3 | 4 | 5 | 6 | 7 | 8 | 9 | 10 | 11 | 12 | 13 | 14 |

← ————————— acids ————————— → ⋮ neutral ⋮ ← ————————— alkalis ————————— →

Universal indicator paper changes colour like this to show the pH of a solution

Reactions to remember

Acids

acid + metal → salt + hydrogen
Example: sulphuric acid + zinc → zinc sulphate + hydrogen

acid + alkali → salt + water
Example: nitric acid + sodium hydroxide → sodium nitrate + water

acid + carbonate → salt + water + carbon dioxide
Example: hydrochloric acid + calcium carbonate → calcium chloride + water + carbon dioxide

Metals

metal + oxygen → metal oxide
Example: aluminium + oxygen → aluminium oxide

metal + water → metal hydroxide + hydrogen
Example: sodium + water → sodium hydroxide + hydrogen

metal + acid → salt + hydrogen
Example: magnesium + sulphuric acid → magnesium sulphate + hydrogen

Non-metals

non-metal + oxygen → non-metal oxide
Example: sulphur + oxygen → sulphur dioxide

Hydrocarbons

hydrocarbon + oxygen → carbon dioxide + water
Example: methane + oxygen → carbon dioxide + water

Respiration in all living things

sugar + oxygen → carbon dioxide + water (and energy)

Photosynthesis in green plants

$$\text{carbon dioxide} + \text{water} \xrightarrow[\text{chlorophyll}]{\text{light}} \text{carbohydrate} + \text{oxygen}$$

Chemical equations

A **chemical equation** is a way of showing what happens in a chemical reaction.

You can have a word equation:

hydrochloric acid + iron ⟶ hydrogen + iron chloride

> This tells you that iron and hydrochloric acid are changed into hydrogen and iron chloride when they react together.

Sometimes, extra little letters called **state symbols** are added in brackets after the names of each chemical.

So you could write:

Hydrochloric acid(aq) + iron(s) ⟶ hydrogen(g) + iron chloride(aq)

State symbols
s = solid
l = liquid
g = gas
aq = aqueous solution (dissolved in water)

Symbol equations tell you exactly what happens to all the atoms in a reaction. For example:

$NaOH(aq) + HCl(aq) \longrightarrow H_2O(l) + NaCl(aq)$

> This tells you that the sodium atom from sodium hydroxide becomes joined to the chlorine atom from hydrochloric acid ...

> ... while the oxygen and hydrogen atoms in the hydroxide part join with hydrogen from the acid to make water.

All the atoms in the reacting chemicals turn up in the products. Atoms cannot suddenly disappear half way through a reaction, or appear from nowhere in the products.

Look at this equation:

magnesium(s) + oxygen(g) ⟶ magnesium oxide(s)
$Mg(s)$ + $O_2(g)$ ⟶ $MgO(s)$
(1 Mg atom) (2 O atoms) (1 Mg and 1 O)

There are 2 atoms of oxygen in a molecule of O_2 on the left of the arrow, but only 1 oxygen atom appears in the magnesium oxide on the right.

An oxygen atom cannot disappear into thin air, so you must *balance* the equation.

Step 1 You can't change the formula of a substance – you can only have more of it.
• Try doubling the amount of MgO in the equation:

$Mg + O_2 \longrightarrow 2MgO$

Now you have 2 atoms of oxygen on both sides of the equation.

Step 2 But now you have 1 Mg on the left, compared with 2 on the right! There must be 2 Mg taking part.
• Add a 2 in front of the Mg on the left of the equation:

$2Mg$ + O_2 ⟶ $2MgO$
(2 Mg) (2 O) (2 Mg + 2 O)

This is now a **balanced equation**.

The periodic table

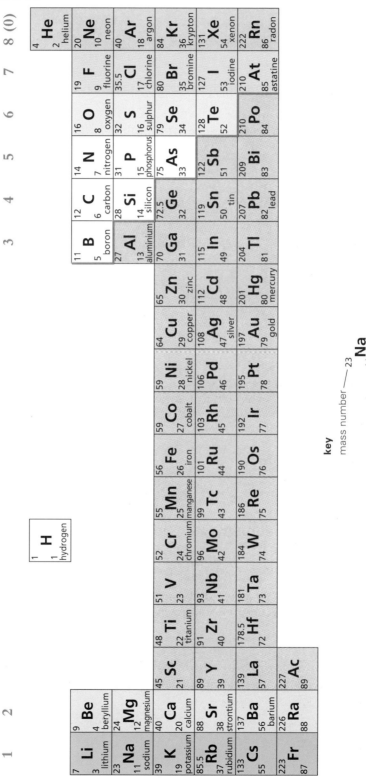

1	2												3	4	5	6	7	8 (0)
																		4 **He** 2 helium
7 **Li** 3 lithium	9 **Be** 4 beryllium												11 **B** 5 boron	12 **C** 6 carbon	14 **N** 7 nitrogen	16 **O** 8 oxygen	19 **F** 9 fluorine	20 **Ne** 10 neon
23 **Na** 11 sodium	24 **Mg** 12 magnesium												27 **Al** 13 aluminium	28 **Si** 14 silicon	31 **P** 15 phosphorus	32 **S** 16 sulphur	35.5 **Cl** 17 chlorine	40 **Ar** 18 argon
39 **K** 19 potassium	40 **Ca** 20 calcium	45 **Sc** 21	48 **Ti** 22 titanium	51 **V** 23	52 **Cr** 24 chromium	55 **Mn** 25 manganese	56 **Fe** 26 iron	59 **Co** 27 cobalt	59 **Ni** 28 nickel	64 **Cu** 29 copper	65 **Zn** 30 zinc		70 **Ga** 31	72.5 **Ge** 32	75 **As** 33	79 **Se** 34	80 **Br** 35 bromine	84 **Kr** 36 krypton
85.5 **Rb** 37 rubidium	88 **Sr** 38 strontium	89 **Y** 39	91 **Zr** 40	93 **Nb** 41	96 **Mo** 42	99 **Tc** 43	101 **Ru** 44	103 **Rh** 45	106 **Pd** 46	108 **Ag** 47 silver	112 **Cd** 48		115 **In** 49	119 **Sn** 50 tin	122 **Sb** 51	128 **Te** 52	127 **I** 53 iodine	131 **Xe** 54 xenon
133 **Cs** 55	137 **Ba** 56 barium	139 **La** 57	178.5 **Hf** 72	181 **Ta** 73	184 **W** 74	186 **Re** 75	190 **Os** 76	192 **Ir** 77	195 **Pt** 78	197 **Au** 79 gold	201 **Hg** 80 mercury		204 **Tl** 81	207 **Pb** 82 lead	209 **Bi** 83	210 **Po** 84	210 **At** 85 astatine	222 **Rn** 86 radon
223 **Fr** 87	226 **Ra** 88	227 **Ac** 89																

1 **H** 1 hydrogen

key

mass number —— 23 **Na**

atomic number —— 11

acids   4.1, 4.2, 4.3, 4.4, 4.5
corrosive liquids with a low pH: they are amongst the most reactive of all substances.

alkali metals   3.4
the name given to the elements in the first group of the periodic table.

alkalis   4.2, 4.4, 4.5
liquids with a high pH: they neutralise acids to make salts.

alkanes   6.9
a group of similar hydrocarbon compounds, including methane; many found in crude oil.

alloy   3.5, 3.12, 6.5
a mixture of metals, e.g. bronze is an alloy of copper and tin.

analysis   1.5
finding out what things are made of.

atom   1.6, 2.4, 2.6, 2.7
the smallest particle that an element can exist as.

atomic number   2.6
the number of protons in an atom.

boiling point   1.8
the temperature at which a liquid turns to a gas.

bond   3.9, 3.10
a chemical joint holding atoms together.

Brownian motion   1.6
small movement of light material like pollen and smoke caused by surrounding molecules bumping into them all the time.

carat   6.5
a measure of the purity of gold.

carbohydrate   5.4, 5.6
compounds of carbon, hydrogen and oxygen: rice, bread and sugar contain carbohydrates.

cast iron   6.3
a brittle form of iron obtained from a blast furnace.

catalyst   3.5, 8.5
a chemical which speeds up a reaction but isn't used up itself.

cement   6.6
a substance mixed with sand and water to produce a very hard building material.

change of state   1.8
a change of material from one state to another, such as melting a solid to a liquid.

chemical change   2.1
a change in which different chemicals are made, which is not easily reversed and includes changes in energy.

chemical equation   2.5
a shorthand way of explaining what happens to chemicals as they react together.

chemical property   4.7
the way a substance reacts with other chemicals.

chlorofluorocarbons   5.1
(CFCs)
a group of chemicals containing carbon, fluorine and chlorine which are released into the air from aerosols and old fridges, damaging the ozone layer.

chlorophyll   5.6
the green material in plants which 'captures' the sunlight.

chromatography   1.5
separating coloured substances.

combustion 2.3, 6.10, 9.4
a reaction where a substance burns in oxygen, giving out heat.

compound 2.4
a pure substance made from at least two types of elements, chemically joined together.

concentration 8.2, 8.3
usually the amount of a substance dissolved in a certain volume of water.

concrete 6.6
a mixture of sand, cement, gravel and water that makes a cheap and strong building material.

condensation 2.1
the process of a gas changing to a liquid as it cools.

conductor 3.3
a material that heat or electricity can pass through easily.

contraction 1.8
the process of things getting smaller, usually as they cool.

core 7.3
the central part of the Earth.

corrosion 4.7, 4.10
the process of rusting, tarnishing or dulling of substances caused by their reaction with air, water or other chemicals.

corrosive 4.1, 4.2
chemicals that attack other materials and destroy them are described as corrosive.

covalent bond 3.10
a way of atoms joining in which electrons are shared.

cracking 6.11
an industrial reaction which breaks big molecules from oil into smaller molecules.

crude oil 6.7, 6.8
a raw material, made from dead plants and animals. Contains a mixture of hydrocarbons.

crust 7.3
the outer surface of the Earth.

crystallisation 1.4
the process of making crystals from a solution by letting the liquid evaporate slowly, leaving the solute to re-appear.

decompose 2.3
break down a chemical substance into smaller bits.

diffusion 1.8, 5.1
the movement or spread of gas or liquid particles from one place towards another.

displacement 4.9, 9.4
a reaction in which one element displaces or removes another element from a compound.

dissolving 1.3
the process of making a solution.

distillation 1.4, 6.8
separating a mixture of liquids by boiling them and then cooling them down.

ductile 3.3
describes something that can easily be drawn out into wires, like a metal.

earthquake 7.1, 7.6
movements of the Earth's surface: mostly happen where two plates collide.

electrodes 6.4
conductors which pass electricity into a liquid: can have a positive (+) or negative (−) charge.

electrolysis 6.4, 8.8, 8.9, 9.4
the process of passing electricity through a liquid to bring about a reaction: usually splitting compounds into elements.

electron 2.6, 2.7
the smallest particle in an atom, with a negative charge and found going round the outside of the atom.

electron configuration 2.7
the way in which electrons are arranged around the outside of an atom.

electron shell 2.7, 3.8, 3.9
a layer or route (orbital) round which electrons travel in an atom.

electroplating 8.9
using electrolysis to coat one metal onto the surface of another metal.

element 2.4, 2.5, 3.1, 3.2
a pure substance made of only one type of atom.

endothermic 8.7, 9.4
reactions which take in heat.

enzyme 8.5, 8.6
a chemical which speeds up reactions in living things.

erosion 7.1
how rocks and soil are worn down by things rubbing against them.

eutrophication 5.9
(pronounced *yu-trofi-kashun*) the loss of oxygen from water caused by rapid growth and decay of algae in rivers and lakes polluted by fertilisers.

evaporation 1.4
one way a liquid turns to a gas (below its boiling point).

excrete 5.4
animals passing out their waste products.

exothermic 8.7, 9.4
reactions which give out heat.

expansion 1.8
the process of a material getting bigger.

extraction 1.4, 6.2, 6.3, 6.4
the process of getting a pure material out of raw materials.

fermentation 8.6
a reaction where sugar changes into alcohol and carbon dioxide, speeded up by enzymes in yeast: used to make bread, beer and wine.

fertiliser 5.7, 5.8, 5.9, 9.3
substance that provides essential nutrients (including nitrogen, potassium and phosphorus) to help plants grow well.

filtration 1.4
one way of separating an insoluble solid from a liquid.

folding 7.2
the squeezing of rock layers, which makes mountains.

formula 2.5, 4.5
a set of symbols that tells you exactly the number of each type of atom in a chemical substance.

fossil fuel 5.4, 6.7
fuel made from dead plants or animals: e.g. coal, crude oil, gas.

fossils 7.2, 7.5
signs of plants or animals trapped when sedimentary rocks were made.

fractional distillation 6.8
liquids in crude oil are boiled and then cooled to separate them into fractions.

fractions 6.8
the different substances found in crude oil.

fuel   **6.8, 6.9, 8.7**
a substance which burns in oxygen and gives
out heat.

gas   **1.7**
a light substance that fills any space it is
put in: its particles are not close, and
move quickly..

giant structure   **3.3, 3.11**
a large number of atoms joined together to
make a substance which is very difficult to
break apart.

group   **3.2**
a family of elements found in the periodic
table, which react in similar ways.

halogens   **3.6, 3.7**
the name given to the non-metals in group 7
of the periodic table.

hydrocarbons   **6.8, 6.9, 6.10, 6.11**
substances made from hydrogen and carbon
only: include petrol, diesel and wax.

igneous   **7.3, 7.4**
a word to describe rock made when hot liquid
rock cools down: you can see crystals in
igneous rocks.

indicator   **4.2**
a substance that changes colour when added
to other substances, to show if they are acid,
alkali or neutral.

inert   **3.8**
a word used to describe a substance that is
unreactive.

insoluble   **1.3**
a substance that will not dissolve in a solvent
is insoluble.

ion   **3.9, 6.4, 8.8**
an atom or group of atoms with a positive (+)
or negative (−) charge.

ionic bond   **3.9**
a way of atoms joining in crystals, by the
giving of electrons from one atom to another.

isotopes   **2.7**
atoms of the same element with different
numbers of neutrons.

lava   **7.3**
hot liquid rock that has come out of a volcano.

liquid   **1.7**
a runny substance that pours from one
container to another: its particles are close
together, and can move around.

litmus   **4.2**
an indicator which is blue in alkalis and red
in acids.

magma   **7.3, 7.6**
hot liquid rock inside the Earth.

malleable   **3.3**
describes something that can be forced to
change shape easily, like a metal.

mantle   **7.3**
part of the Earth, between the outer crust and
inner core.

mass number   **2.6**
the total number of protons and neutrons in
an atom.

material   **1.1, 1.2, 6.13**
another word for a substance.

melting point   **1.5, 1.8**
the temperature at which a substance turns
from solid to liquid.

metamorphic   **7.4**
a word to describe rock made by heating and
squeezing another rock inside the Earth.

mineral   6.1
a naturally occurring material from within the Earth which might be useful.

mixture   1.2, 1.4
a mixture contains several different substances that can usually be separated: they are not joined together by chemical bonds.

molecule   2.4, 2.5
a particle made from at least two atoms joined together.

natural gas   6.7, 6.8
a raw material found with crude oil: chemical name methane.

neutral   4.2
not acidic or alkaline: a substance which is pH7, like pure water.

neutralisation   4.4, 4.6, 9.4
a process of making a substance neutral (pH 7), such as adding an acid to an alkali.

neutron   2.6
a particle found in the nucleus of an atom, with no charge.

nitrogen fixing   5.7
the way plants obtain the nitrogen nutrients they need from other sources of nitrogen.

noble gases   3.8, 5.2
the name given to elements in group 8 in the periodic table, containing unreactive gases.

non-biodegradable   8.1
materials that won't rot away, such as plastics.

non-renewable   6.7
describes fuels which are being used up much faster than they are being made: coal, crude oil, natural gas.

nucleus   2.6
the centre of an atom, containing protons and neutrons.

orbital   2.7
a particular pathway or shell of electrons round an atom.

ore   6.1, 6.3, 9.3
a mineral which contains a useful material like a metal that can be extracted from it.

oxidation   2.3, 4.8, 9.4
a reaction in which oxygen is added to a substance, such as burning or corrosion.

ozone layer   5.1
a layer of gas which protects the Earth from the harmful ultra-violet rays of the Sun.

particle   1.6, 1.7, 1.8, 2.6
a term describing atoms or molecules – the small pieces of matter, from which all materials are made.

period   3.2
a row of elements across the periodic table.

periodic table   3.2, 3.12, 4.5
a special way of classifying or arranging elements.

pH scale   4.2
the pH scale measures the strength of acids and alkalis: it goes from strong acid 1 to strong alkali 14, with 7 being neutral.

photosynthesis   5.4, 5.6
the way plants use sunlight to change water and carbon dioxide into food for their growth.

physical change   2.1
a change in which different chemicals are not formed, and which is easily reversed.

physical properties   4.7
facts about a substance which can be seen and measured like strength, density, melting point.

plastics   6.11, 6.12
group of materials made from crude oil: molecules are long chains.

plate boundary   7.6
where two plates collide or move apart: volcanoes and earthquakes are likely when they collide.

plates   7.6
parts of the Earth's surface, which move very slowly.

pollutants   5.1
chemicals which harm the environment.

polymer   6.11, 6.12
a long-chain molecule, e.g. in plastics.

porous   6.7
describes a solid material with holes inside which can soak up liquids.

product   2.2
a substance made in a chemical reaction.

properties   1.2
the qualities or characteristics of a substance.

proton   2.6
a particle found in the nucleus of an atom, with a positive charge.

pure substance   1.2
a material containing only one type of particle.

purify   1.4
to make something pure so that it consists of a single substance.

rate of reaction   8.1, 8.2, 8.3, 8.4
a measurement of how quickly a reaction happens.

raw material   1.1, 6.1, 8.9
a natural material got from the ground, plants or animals, from which other materials are made.

reactant   2.2
a substance that is used up in a chemical reaction.

reaction   2.1, 2.2, 2.3, 9.4
the process of changing substances into different ones.

reactivity series   4.8, 4.9, 4.10, 6.2
a list of metals given in the order in which they react with other chemicals: the most reactive is at the top.

recycling   6.4, 6.12, 6.13
collecting, processing and re-using useful materials.

reduction   6.2, 6.3, 9.4
a reaction in which oxygen is removed from a compound.

reinforce   6.6
add an extra material to increase the strength of another.

relative atomic mass   9.2, 9.3
a number comparing how heavy each type of atom is: hydrogen, the lightest atom, has a value of 1.

relative formula mass   9.2, 9.3
a number comparing the heaviness of compounds, often called relative molecular mass.

respiration   5.4
how living things use oxygen to get energy from food.

reversible reaction   5.8, 9.4
a chemical reaction that can go one way to make the products, but can also go back the other way to remake the starting materials.

rust   4.3, 4.10
a brown oxide of iron formed when iron reacts with air and moisture.

salts   4.3, 4.6
substances which are made when acids are neutralised: they are usually solid crystals which are soluble in water.

sedimentary   7.2, 7.4
a word to describe rock formed from tiny pieces squashed together: sedimentary rocks often contain fossils.

semiconductor   3.12
a material that conducts electricity only slightly or under special conditions, like silicon.

semi-metal   3.12
a material that has some of the properties of metals and some of non-metals.

solid   1.7
a substance with its own shape, with its particles close and joined together.

soluble   1.3
a substance that will dissolve in a solvent is said to be soluble.

solute   1.3
a substance that dissolves in a solution.

solution   1.3
a mixture in which one substance dissolves in another, such as salt in water.

solvent   1.3
a liquid that dissolves things.

states of matter   1.7
solids, liquids and gases: the three forms in which materials exist.

steel   3.5, 6.3
an alloy of iron with small amounts of other metals or non-metals mixed in, such as carbon, chromium or tungsten.

surface area   8.2, 8.3
the size of the outer part of a solid/how much of a solid can be attacked by moving particles: breaking a solid into smaller bits makes a bigger surface area.

suspension   1.3
a mixture in which small particles of a solid do not dissolve in a liquid.

symbol   2.5
one or two letters used as shorthand for an element.

synthetic material   1.1
a material like plastic that is manufactured and is not directly obtained from the ground, plants or animals.

thermal decomposition   2.3, 6.11, 9.4
the breaking down of a substance into simpler substances as it is heated.

transition metals   3.2, 3.5
a large group of metals in the centre of the periodic table.

trend   3.4
a gradual change in properties of elements as you go up or down a group in the periodic table.

universal indicator   4.2
an indicator with colours ranging from red in acids, green in neutral solutions and dark purple in alkalis.

weathering   7.1
how rain, wind, ice and snow break tiny bits off rock.

yeast   8.6
living thing which contains useful enzymes: used to make beer, bread and wine by fermentation.